CW00539188

A key to the major groups of British terrestrial invertebrates

Second Edition

By S.M. Tilling

FSC

BRINGING
ENVIRONMENTAL
UNDERSTANDING TO ALL

First Edition 1987. Second Edition 2014.
© FSC 1987, 2014
ISBN 978 1 90881 920 8
Publication code OP167

Acknowledgements

First Edition, 1987

Thanks are due to Dr John Crothers who administered the 'testing' of a preliminary version of this guide and edited the manuscripts and proofs. Also, to the many people who took the trouble to use the key and return their comments; without their efforts the guide would undoubtedly have floundered. Dr Henry Disney scrutinised the early versions, and was supportive throughout. The fact that Indonesian fauna still fail to key out is entirely my fault. Dr David Harding and Mr R. G. Middleton permitted me to use and copy from their drawings of the elusive cased caddis fly larva. Thanks also to Dr David Sheppard and the Nature Conservancy Council for lending me a specimen of a cased beetle larva. Lastly, I am grateful to the anonymous trust and the Field Studies Council for the financial and administrative support which has enabled the AIDGAP project to survive.

Second Edition, 2014

This AIDGAP key was first published in *Field Studies* **6**(4): 695-766 in 1987, and has remained in print ever since. For the Second Edition, the taxonomy and references have been comprehensively updated. I am particularly grateful to Paul Lee and Philip Wheater, who provided suggestions for improvements, both drawing on their many years of experience of using the First Edition with students. Thanks also to Peter Boardman, Sue Townsend, Richard Burkmar and Simon Norman of the Field Studies Council, who have also made useful comments on the text.

Contents

Introduction

One of the most frustrating of problems facing biologists who are attempting serious survey work for the first time is knowing where to start in describing and interpreting their data. Untangling the diversity of animals encountered in terrestrial habitats may seem a daunting task, but it is usually possible with sufficient commitment and patience. Identification, an integral part of such work, may seem the most difficult obstacle, particularly when dealing with small invertebrates. Frequently, this is due to the absence of a simple key rather than to any insuperable taxonomic problems. This key has been written with beginners in mind and should help to minimise the problems in identification. A preliminary draft – the 'test' version – was subjected to extended trials by a wide range of readers, and this version has been revised in the light of their comments. However, no key is flawless and problems will undoubtedly exist in this version. The AIDGAP project's co-ordinator would welcome suggestions which could be incorporated in any future editions.

All terrestrial invertebrates larger than 1 mm found in the British Isles – and many that are smaller – are included and identification is based on external characters which are visible with a hand lens, or a low-power binocular microscope. I have chosen to interpret the key's title very loosely. Thus, the major groups included here encompass several that are not strictly 'native' to the British Isles, but which may be encountered nevertheless – scorpions and stick insects, for example. Many animals which are predominantly parasitic, or otherwise narrowly restricted by their mode of life, are included because they will be collected using conventional sampling techniques. Invertebrates that are found exclusively in marine or freshwater habitats are omitted, but groups that live predominantly in such environments but are found occasionally in terrestrial habitats are covered. However, habitat-based separations are notoriously difficult and readers may feel that additional groups should be included. The AIDGAP project would be interested in any such suggestions, or others that may help to improve the key.

It should be possible to identify most invertebrates without killing them. Remember that many are now protected by law and conservation should always be a priority. One way in which small individuals can be observed without killing is by using a specially manufactured 'bug box'. This consists of a small transparent dish (a petri dish, for example), inlaid with a perspex sheet which has different diameter holes drilled through it. Animals can be placed in the appropriate-sized recess and the lid replaced. By turning the dish over, the upper and lower surface of the specimen can be examined. Another method is to confine the animal to the corner of a perspex box or dish by using a piece of tissue or plasticine pressed into place.

Many smaller invertebrates can be temporarily 'stunned' by placing them in a refrigerator – but not for too long!

A set of notes is given for each group at the back of the guide (p. 52 onwards) and these will provide an introduction to the ecology of the animals, whilst the lists of references will enable the reader to continue with further research and identification.

How to use the key

The key is arranged in the traditional dichotomous form. At each stage readers have to make a choice between two contrasting descriptions. Depending on their choice, they will be directed either to the name of the taxonomic group or to another couplet in the key. Readers who are unfamiliar with the layout of the guide should always start at couplet A1 in KEY A and read both descriptions before proceeding to the next stage. For example, if in couplet A1 you have decided that the animal has jointed legs go to couplet A2; if the creature has three pairs of jointed legs go to couplet A3; and so on. Eventually, you will be directed to a new key. At times, you may go backwards, but persevere and you will arrive at an answer.

The illustrations. Wherever possible the illustrations are taken from living and preserved specimens. However, many of the drawings are stylised, to give a composite impression of a group's appearance and will, therefore, not closely resemble the identified specimens. This is inevitable in groups which may contain several thousand species. Some experts will blanch when seeing the caricatures of their chosen group. My only excuse is that the keys are aimed at those with little or no experience. If in doubt, consult one of the texts given in the notes at the back of the guide; the books by Chinery (1986), dealing with adult insects, and Cloudsley-Thompson & Sankey (1961), dealing with non-insect groups, are comprehensive and are particularly useful.

Please read the information notes. These are included throughout the key and will help you in making decisions. You will find that you need to refer to these less and less as your expertise increases. Readers who have used the guide several times will be able to go directly to the appropriate key. When identification has been accomplished go to the back of the guide; the notes given there should confirm your identification, or will help in spotting any obvious discrepancies.

Warning. Beware of damaged specimens. Invertebrates are usually very fragile, and may easily loose appendages – such as tails, antennae. Critical parts of the keys are highlighted by notes in the text, but try not to mis-handle the animals.

Classification list

The following table lists the groups which are included in the key. *Italics* indicate the taxonomic level to which each group is taken (see Taxonomy, p. 52).

Phylum	Subphylum	Class	Subclass	Order	Suborder
NEMATODA					
NEMATOMORPHA					
PLATYHELMINTHES		*Turbellaria*			
NEMERTEA					
ANNELIDA		*Hirudinea*			
		Oligochaeta			
ARTHROPODA	Chelicerata	Arachnida		*Scorpiones*	
				Pseudoscorpiones	
				Araneae	
				Opiliones	
			Acari		
	Crustacea	Malacostraca		*Isopoda*	
				Amphipoda	

Phylum	Subphylum	Class	Subclass	Order	Suborder
		Maxilopoda		Copepoda	
	Myriapoda	Pauropoda			
		Diplopoda		Chordeumatida	Craspedosomatidea
					Chordeumatidea
				Julida	
				Glomerida	
				Polydesmida	
				Polyzoniida	
				Polyxenida	
		Chilopoda		Geophilomorpha	
				Lithobiomorpha	
				Scolopendromorpha	
		Symphyla			
	Hexapoda	Entognatha		Collembola	
				Diplura	
				Protura	
				Collembola	
		Insecta		Archeaognatha	
				Zygentoma	
				Ephemeroptera	
				Odonata	Anisoptera
					Zygoptera
				Dermaptera	
				Orthoptera	
				Phasmida	
				Plecoptera	
				Hemiptera	
				Phthiraptera	
				Pscoptera	
				Thysanoptera	
				Coleoptera	
				Diptera	
				Hymenoptera	Symphyta
					Apocrita
				Lepidoptera	
				Mecoptera	
				Megaloptera	
				Neuroptera	
				Raphidioptera	
				Siphonaptera	
				Strepsiptera	
				Trichoptera	
MOLLUSCA		Gastropoda		Prosobranchia	
				Pulmonata	

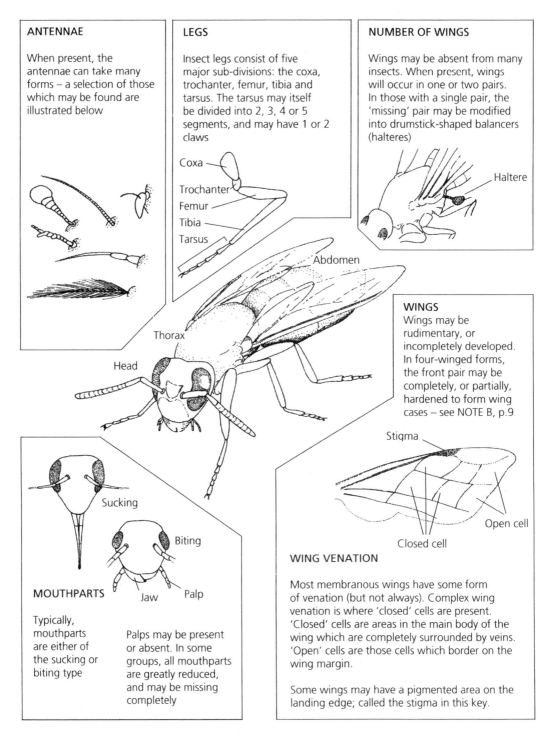

ANTENNAE

When present, the antennae can take many forms – a selection of those which may be found are illustrated below

LEGS

Insect legs consist of five major sub-divisions: the coxa, trochanter, femur, tibia and tarsus. The tarsus may itself be divided into 2, 3, 4 or 5 segments, and may have 1 or 2 claws

Coxa
Trochanter
Femur
Tibia
Tarsus

NUMBER OF WINGS

Wings may be absent from many insects. When present, wings will occur in one or two pairs. In those with a single pair, the 'missing' pair may be modified into drumstick-shaped balancers (halteres)

Haltere

Abdomen

Thorax

Head

WINGS
Wings may be rudimentary, or incompletely developed. In four-winged forms, the front pair may be completely, or partially, hardened to form wing cases – see NOTE B, p.9

Stigma

Open cell

Closed cell

Sucking

Biting

MOUTHPARTS

Jaw   Palp

Typically, mouthparts are either of the sucking or biting type

Palps may be present or absent. In some groups, all mouthparts are greatly reduced, and may be missing completely

WING VENATION

Most membranous wings have some form of venation (but not always). Complex wing venation is where 'closed' cells are present. 'Closed' cells are areas in the main body of the wing which are completely surrounded by veins. 'Open' cells are those cells which border on the wing margin.

Some wings may have a pigmented area on the landing edge; called the stigma in this key.

Figure 1. External features of a typical insect.

Glossary

ABDOMEN One of the major body divisions; lying behind the HEAD and THORAX in insects. Usually carrying the digestive and reproductive organs.

ANTENNA (plural *antennae*) Modified front appendage, carrying sensory structures.

ALATE With wings.

APTEROUS Lacking wings.

BIFURCATE Splitting into two branches.

BILOBED With two lobes.

BRACHYPTEROUS Short-winged.

CARAPACE Part of the exoskeleton, forming a shield-like structure which covers the HEAD and THORAX in arachnids and crustaceans.

CEPHALOTHORAX A division of the body where the THORAX is fused with the HEAD, found in subphyla Chelicerata and Crustacea.

CHRYSALIS The hardened pupal case in metamorphosing insects (see ENDOPTERYGOTA).

CLITELLUM A band of enlarged fused segments in earthworms; a source of mucus for protecting eggs and nourishing embryos.

CONIFEROUS Cone-bearing trees, often characterised by needle-like leaves (e.g. pine needles).

COXA (plural *coxae*). A segment of the leg, closest to the body (see Fig. 1).

DECIDUOUS Trees, mainly broad-leaved, that lose their leaves in the winter.

DISTAL The end of an appendage which is outermost from the body.

DORSAL The upper surface.

ELYTRON (plural *elytra*) The modified front wing of an insect, forming a hardened or leathery protective case for the membranous hind wing which is used for flight and is usually folded underneath. In some insects the elytra may be short, whilst in others they may be fused together (in which case the insect has lost the ability to fly).

ENCYSTING Forming a protective case, often within a gelatinous coat. This is usually a dormant stage during which development is suspended, and often functions as a protection against adverse conditions.

ENDOPTERYGOTA The more advanced of the winged insects; undergoing a rapid metamorphosis. The wings develop internally in the larva which enters a pupal stage during which it metamorphoses into the adult.

EXOPTERYGOTA The more primitive of the winged insects; undergoing a gradual metamorphosis in which the wings develop externally on the nymph which, in most groups, looks increasingly like the adult as it undergoes a series of moults.

FEMUR One of the segments of the arthropod leg (see Fig. 1).

FLAGELLUM The delicate hair-like extension of an antenna, usually arising from two or three thickened basal segments.

FORCIPULE The large poison claw on the underside of the head. Appears to be part of the mouthparts but is formed by the modified front leg of a centipede.

HALTERE Modified insect wing, reduced to a small drumstick-shaped organ which helps to balance the animal in flight.

HEAD One of the major body divisions. Lying at the front of the body; usually carrying the major neural organs, most advanced sense organs (although this is not always the case) and mouthparts.

HEAD CAPSULE Usually used to describe a larval/nymphal head which is encapsulated in a hard chitinous case, usually with external palps and other mouthparts, and antennae. This contrasts with the larvae of some advanced insects in which the head capsule has been lost and most external appendages are vestigial or have become enclosed in the fleshy head which can often be retracted into the body behind.

JOINTED LEGS The 'true' legs which arise from the THORAX; not to be confused with abdominal PROLEGS.

LARVA (plural *larvae*) The immature stage of arthropods which undergo a complete metamorphosis, i.e. where there is no resemblance to the adult. For terrestrial arthropod groups this refers mainly to the juveniles of the endopterygote insects. The larval stage is followed by pupation during which the animal undergoes the often striking transformation into the adult form.

LATERALLY COMPRESSED Flattened from side-to-side.

MEMBRANOUS Transparent and fragile, in contrast to much of the exoskeleton of most arthropods, which consists of tough and deeply pigmented cuticle.

MESOTHORAX The middle (second) of the three thoracic segments (see THORAX).

METATHORAX The hind-most of the three thoracic segments (see THORAX).

NECK The junction between the HEAD and the THORAX.

NYMPH The immature stage of arthropods which do not undergo complete metamorphosis, i.e. the majority of the arthropods, excluding the ENDOPTERYGOTA. The nymphs increasingly resemble the adults as they undergo a series of moults (gradual metamorphosis).

PALP A segmented mouthpart, usually carrying chemo-sensitive cells (the arthropod equivalent of the tastebuds).

PEDICEL The narrow waist separating the CEPHALOTHORAX from the ABDOMEN in spiders, and the THORAX and ABDOMEN in Hymenoptera (although it is in fact the modified second abdominal segment in these insects).

PEDIPALP Segmented structure in arachnids, usually held in front of the head. It may appear leg-like, or can be modified into claws in scorpions and pseudoscorpions or into a sperm transferring organ in male spiders.

PHORESY Behaviour whereby an animal attaches itself to another animal for purposes of transport, i.e. hitching a lift.

PROBOSCIS Usually refers to the sucking tube-like mouthparts in bugs (order Hemiptera), but is sometimes used incorrectly to describe any snout-like feature projecting from the front of the head (see ROSTRUM).

PROLEG A fleshy abdominal appendage found on caterpillars and other insect larvae. Although prolegs may be quite large, they are not true jointed legs (which are always attached to the THORAX).

PRONOTUM The upper surface of the prothorax.

PROTHORAX The front-most of the three thoracic divisions (see THORAX).

PUPA (plural *pupae*) The life-history stage immediately preceding the adult stage in the ENDOPTERYGOTA. It is during this stage that the insects undergo the metamorphosis from LARVA into adult. Usually, the pupa is inactive but in some groups it may be temporarily active.

ROSTRUM A beak-like extension to the HEAD and/or mouthparts, found mainly in bugs (Order Hemiptera) and weevils (Order Coleoptera).

SCALE A modified hair, forming a flattened plate-like structure. The differently coloured scales may give a striking coloration in butterflies and some moths. Also found in other animals, e.g. silverfish (Order Thysanura).

SECONDARY SEGMENTATION See SEGMENT below.

SEGMENT A section of the body of invertebrates, either of the main body or of the appendages (legs, palps, etc.). The segments are sometimes divided by visible joints, but in many invertebrates the underlying body segmentation may be hidden. Conversely, some animals may have 'secondary' segments. These appear as true segments, with clear joints in between, but are in fact artefacts of surface ornamentation and do not reflect any 'real' underlying body segmentation.

STIGMA A dark spot on the forewings of insects, usually approximately half-way along the leading edge or close to the distal tip of the wing.

TARSUS One of the major divisions of the arthropod leg. The outermost (distal) segment, which may itself be sub-divided into smaller segments (up to a maximum of five) (see Fig. 1).

TARSAL SEGMENTS The sub-segments which form the TARSUS; up to five in number (see TARSUS, and Fig. 1).

TIBIA (plural *tibiae*) One of the major divisions of the arthropod leg. In insects, it is the penultimate (second from last) segment (see Fig. 1).

THORAX One of the major body divisions in the arthropods. In the insects it is the middle of three divisions, lying behind the HEAD and in front of the ABDOMEN. The major locomotory appendages arise from it, i.e. the legs and wings. In other arthropods the thorax may be fused with the head, to form the CEPHALOTHORAX. In insects, the thorax is itself divided into three sub-divisions – the pro-, meso- and metathorax.

VENTRAL The lower side.

VESTIGIAL Not fully developed.

Identification keys

KEY A
INTRODUCTORY KEY

A1   'True' jointed legs present A2
                              (see NOTE A opposite)

–   No 'true' jointed legs . . . . **KEY B**
                                        (page 10)
                              (see NOTE A opposite)

A2   Three pairs of *jointed* legs A3

      Note. If your animal apparently has two pairs of legs,
      go to A3.

–   More than three pairs of true *jointed* legs (see
      NOTE A opposite) . . . . **KEY C**
                                        (page 16)

A3   Wings present A4
                              (see NOTE B opposite)

–   Wings absent . . . . **KEY D**
                                        (page 22)
                              (see NOTE B opposite)

A4   One pair of wings . . . . **KEY E**
                                        (page 40)

      Note. In many insects having one pair of wings the
      second pair are reduced to two small drumstick-shaped
      appendages – the halteres (a). If halteres are present
      assume that your animal has one pair of wings and go
      to KEY E.

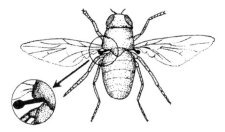

a

–   Two pairs of wings . . . . **KEY F**
                                        (page 42)

      Note. Include all animals which have hardened or
      leathery upper wing cases, or incompletely developed
      wing pads (see NOTE B opposite), as having two pairs
      of wings.

NOTE A: LEGS

Look carefully. The most likely source of confusion here will be with maggot- or caterpillar-like larvae. If jointed legs are present in these animals there will always be three pairs (a), and these will be situated immediately behind the head. Fleshy stumps – prolegs or 'claspers' – may also appear further down the body but these are not true jointed legs (b).

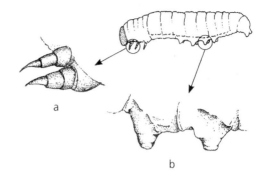

NOTE B: WINGS

Wings can be difficult to see and one mistake in particular is commonly made. In some insects the first pair are modified into hardened or leathery wing cases which protect the second pair of wings. These cases – the elytra – may be deeply pigmented and difficult to distinguish from the rest of the body. If in doubt, try teasing the suspected elytra apart and this will usually show whether or not they are really wing cases (a & b). The wing cases have become fused in some groups and will not be moved. Look for the 'join' down the back (c); if this is present assume that the animal has two pairs of wings. In other groups the elytra may be very short (d), whilst in immature (nymphal) stages the wings may be incompletely developed and are easily overlooked (e & f). If short elytra or immature wing pads are present count the specimen as having two pairs of wings. Hymenoptera have two pairs of wings, but in some specimens the forewings appear to be 'zipped' together with the hindwings. Don't worry, where there is doubt the animals will key out both ways.

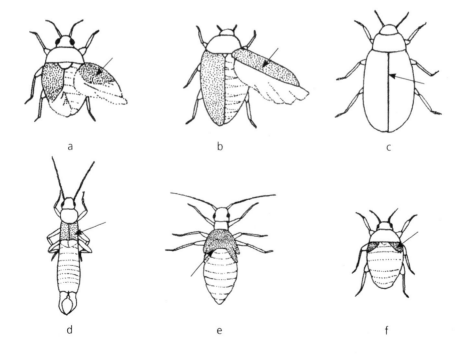

KEY B
ANIMALS WITH NO TRUE JOINTED LEGS.
NO WINGS

B1   Shell present (snails and some slugs) B2

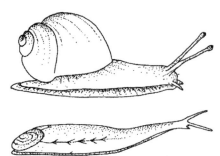

–   No shell B3

This couplet will only work with living or recently dead animals

B2   Body, when withdrawn into the shell, is protected by a hard and horny cover – the *operculum* . . . .
'Gilled' snails
PROSOBRANCHIA
(p. 75)

–   The body, when withdrawn into the shell, is not protected by an operculum or the body cannot be fully withdrawn into the shell . . . . .
'Lunged' slugs and snails
PULMONATA
(p. 75)

Note. Living snails may seal their shells with a thin film when resting during the day. This seal may be thicker and more opaque during times of drought, or when the snail is hibernating during the winter. Don't confuse this temporary seal – the epiphragm – with the operculum which is a permanent feature. If in doubt, prod the covering with a pencil; an epiphragm will break, an operculum won't.

B3   Body not obviously segmented. With or without head tentacles B4

–   Body obviously segmented – never with head tentacles. (Do not confuse segmented antennae with non-segmented tentacles.) B7

B4   Two sets of head tentacles. The upper pair are
     longer than the lower and may appear clubbed,
     sometimes with dark 'eye' spots at their tips (a).
     Lower body with a 'foot' fringe (b) . . . . . **Slugs**
                                    PULMONATA
                                         (p. 75)

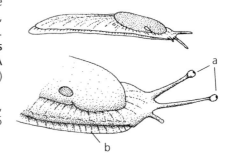

–   No such head tentacles, or if 'horns' are present,
     then there is no flattened 'foot' fringe B5

B5   Body is long and thin – many times longer than
     broad. Not flattened in cross-section (c). Never
     moves by 'gliding' over the substrate, and cannot
     alter the body width during movement . . . . .
              Hairworms and eelworms
            NEMATODA and **NEMATOMORPHA**
              (difficult to separate, see notes on p. 53)

–   Body flattened in cross-section (d, e), in part at
     least (if in doubt look at the lower part of the
     body – the *sole*). Animal moves by 'gliding'
     over the substrate, and when active it can
     contract and extend its body to several times its
     'normal' resting length B6

B6   Eyes arranged in two groups, with 3 or 8 eyes in each (a); never with two large eyes only. Can extend the proboscis from the head when alive (b). Two longitudinal darker stripes pass down the whole length of the body . . . . . . **Ribbon worm**
NEMERTEA
(p. 54)

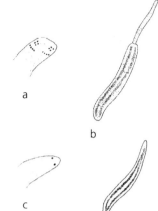

a

b

–   Eyes not arranged in two groups of 3 or 8 eyes; either numerous eyes scattered over front end, or two single eyes (c). No proboscis (the mouth opens on the ventral surface). No longitudinal stripes, or if present, these merge or fade well short of the head end (d) . . . .
Free-living flatworms
TURBELLARIA
(p. 53)

c

d

Note. Care should be taken here. Only one British species of ribbon worm, *Argonemertes dendyi*, has been recorded and is thought to be very rare. Make sure that you haven't got the similar flatworm, *Microplana terrestris*, which has no proboscis.

B7   Fewer than 20 body segments B8

–   More than 20 body segments B15

B8   Has a distinct head capsule, although this may be partly retracted into the body behind (if in doubt, look for antennae and external mouthparts. One, or both, of these structures will be present in animals with a head capsule) B9

–   No head capsule apparent B14

B9   The body segment immediately behind the head
      is much larger than the two following it, its length
      being equal to, or longer than, their combined
      length (a, b) . . . .
            Larvae of wood and bark boring beetles
                              COLEOPTERA
                                  (p. 69)

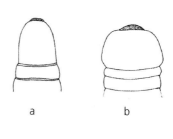

−   The three segments behind the head are
      approximately equal in size, or if one of the
      three segments behind the head is larger than
      the other two, it is not the one immediately
      behind the head (c) B10

B10   The body is not covered in long bristles or spines
      . . . . B11

−   The body is covered by long bristles or spines
      – some being as long as, or longer than, the
      width of the abdominal segments B12

B11   The long axis of the head (in side profile) points
      downwards (or slightly forwards) with mouthparts
      also pointing downwards or slightly forwards so
      that they are not visible when viewed from above
      the head (c) . . . .
                        Weevil (beetle) larvae
                              COLEOPTERA
                                  (p. 69)

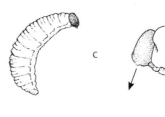

−   The long axis of the head and the mouthparts
      points forwards (d). The mouth parts can be seen
      from above . . . . **True fly larvae**
                                  DIPTERA
                                  (p. 70)

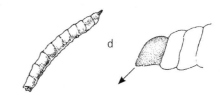

Note: These two groups can be very difficult to
distinguish; if in doubt consult a specialist textbook (see
the notes on p. 70-71). Weevil larvae are vegetarian,
and will most often be found in rolled leaves, amongst
roots, or tunnelling under bark, in stems or in nuts.
Diptera larvae may be carnivorous or omnivorous and
will be found almost anywhere.

B12 Animals associated with a nest or refuge belonging to a mammal or a bird B13

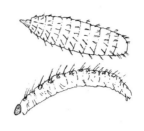

– Animal not associated with a nest or refuge
. . . . **True fly larvae**
DIPTERA
(p. 70)

B13 Pale and worm-like. Long bristles in single bands encircling each segment. Prominent one-segmented antenna. Thirteen body segments (not including the head); all 'simple', lacking any surface structure (prolegs, suction pads, etc.) except the last (anal) segment which has a pair of tube-like extensions . . . . **Flea larvae**
SIPHONAPTERA
(p. 74)

– Without this combination of characters . . . .
True fly larvae
DIPTERA
(p. 70)

B14 Darker pigmented 'skeletal' structures can be seen inside the head end. The animal may have lobes, bristles or tail-like extensions on its body, but not always (see Fig. 2, p. 15) . . . .
True fly larvae
DIPTERA
(p. 70)

Note: Although these structures, internal mouthparts, are usually highlighted against the pale flesh they are easier to see if the animal is gently squeezed between two microscope slides.

– No darker internal structures visible in the head, even when squeezing the animal. Never with long lobes, bristles or tail-like extensions . . . .
Bee, ant or wasp larvae
HYMENOPTERA (Apocrita)
(p. 71)

Internal mouthparts

Head

a

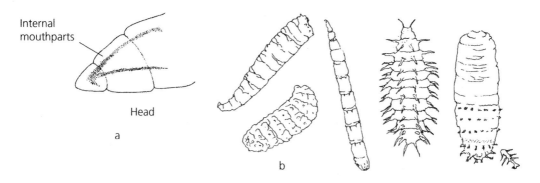

b

Figure 2. Diptera larvae. (a) Close-up of a head, (b) a range of whole larvae (From Skidmore, 1985).

B15 Suckers present, usually at both ends of the body. No clitellum . . . . **Leeches HIRUDINEA** (p. 54)

— No suckers present on the body. There may be a band, formed by fused segments, part-way along the body (the *clitellum*) B16

B16 More than 30 body segments. There may be a band, formed by fused segments, part-way along the body (the clitellum) . . . . **Earthworms and potworms OLIGOCHAETA** (p. 54)

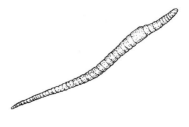

— Less than 30 body segments. No clitellum. See Figure 2 also . . . . **True fly larvae DIPTERA** (p. 70)

Note. Dipterous larvae which appear to have more than 15 body segments are displaying 'secondary' segmentation – see the Glossary (p. 7). Also, if you look closely you will probably see a head capsule which has been overlooked previously.

KEY C
ANIMALS WITH MORE THAN THREE PAIRS OF JOINTED LEGS. NO WINGS

C1   More than four pairs of jointed legs. Antennae present or absent C2

–   Four pairs of jointed legs. No antennae C16

C2   Two pairs of antennae obviously present, clearly separated at the base. The body is flattened side-to-side to give a shrimp-like appearance . . . . .
      Sandhoppers or scuds
      AMPHIPODA
      (p. 58)

      Note: Another group of crustaceans, the copepods, may be found in leaf litter. Always smaller than 1 mm, these will have two pairs of antennae of which the upper is the larger; in the sandhoppers (above) the lower is the largest (see notes on p. 59).

–   Only a single pair of antennae clearly present, or antennae absent C3

C3   Antennae clearly branched, with branches originating some way from the base (a). Less than 2 mm long . . . . **PAUROPODA**
      (p. 60)

–   Antennae unbranched, or absent. Often larger than 2 mm C4

C4   Body relatively broad in dorsal view; length never more than three times the width. The living animal may roll into an almost spherical ball when disturbed C5

–   Body relatively narrow in dorsal view; length greater than three times the width. Although the living animal may curl up, it never rolls into a tight ball C6

C5   6 or 7 pairs of walking legs. Looking from above, the hind end of the body terminates in a series of short abdominal segments, usually with projections (uropods) . . . . **Woodlice ISOPODA**
(p. 58)

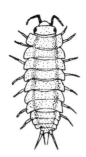

Note. The woodlice are crustaceans (see p. 58), and, consequently, have two pairs of antennae. However, one pair is minute and easily overlooked and has been ignored in this key, to help ease-of-use.

–   Up to 17 pairs of legs. Body never terminates in a series of narrow abdominal segments. (Beware! See the note on pillbugs below) . . . .
Pill millipedes GLOMERIDA
(p. 59)

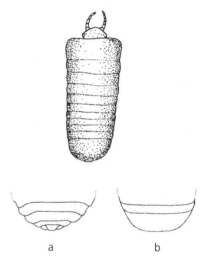

Note. The pillbug woodlice, *Armadillidium* spp., may easily be confused with the pill millipedes. Both can roll into a ball. The pillbug woodlice have narrow terminal abdominal segments (a), whereas these are absent in the millipedes (b). Another millipede – *Polyxenus lagurus* – may key out here. This species is covered in a series of hair tufts, unlike the pill millipedes which are smooth (see C10).

a   b

C6   One pair of legs per body segment. Antennae long – more than 14 segments (in adults) C7

Note. Make sure that you are looking at the right end! Some centipedes have terminal abdominal appendages which look like antennae but have less than 6 segments.

–   Two pairs of legs per body segment. Antennae relatively short – never more than 8 segments
Millipedes DIPLOPODA C10

C7   Less than 15 mm long. Never more than 12 pairs
     of legs. Front legs not modified into a set of
     posion claws . . . . **SYMPHYLA**
                                                  (p. 61)

     Note. Very rarely, recently hatched immature centipedes
     may key out here. These will have a pair of poison claws
     on the underside of the head, but may have as few as
     four pairs of legs; the others are added as the juvenile
     undergoes a series of moults.

–   Up to 75 mm long. Often with many more than
     12 pairs of legs. Front legs modified into a pair of
     posion claws (forcipules, a)
     CHILOPODA Centipedes C8

Underside
of head

C8   7 to 15 pairs of legs . . . .
                         Surface-dwelling centipedes
                         LITHOBIOMORPHA
                                                  (p. 61)

–   More than 20 pairs of legs C9

C9   21 pairs of legs (may lose the last pair of legs if
     mishandled). Fast moving . . . .
                         Surface-dwelling centipedes
                         SCOLOPENDROMORPHA
                                                  (p. 61)

–   31 to 80 pairs of legs. Slow moving . . . .
                         Soil-living or surface dwelling centipedes
                         GEOPHILOMORPHA
                                                  (p. 61)

C10 Surface of each body segment bearing two transverse rows of spines, with two clumps of bristles. Last segment with two very dense brushes of rearward facing bristles . . . .
'Bristly' millipedes
POLYXENIDA
(p. 60)

– Without the arrangement of spines and bristles described above C11

C11 With keel-like extensions to the side of each body segment, giving the upper part of each segment a flattened appearance in cross-section (a, b). When viewed from above, the outline of the body is deeply serrated (c) C12

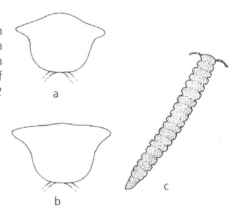

a

b

c

– Without keel-like extensions on the sides of the body segments. Often approximately circular in cross section (d), but if flattened, then there are no keels (e) and the body outline is not deeply serrated in profile (when viewed from above) (f, g) C13

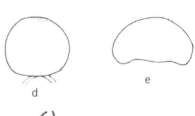

d

e

C12 Adults with a maximum of 20 body segments . . .
Flat-backed millipedes
POLYDESMIDA
(p. 60)

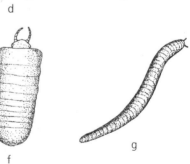

f

g

– Adults with up to 30 body segments . . . .
Millipedes
CHORDEUMATIDA
(suborder Craspedosomatidea)
(p. 60)

C13   The upper surface of each body segment forms
      a roof-like dome. The millipede appears flattened
      in cross-section (a, b), with body width (not
      including legs) more than 1.5 times the body
      depth (not including legs) C14

–   The upper surface of each body segment does
      not form a roof-like dome. Often approximately
      circular in cross-section (c); body width roughly
      equal to body depth, never exceeding the
      ratio of 1.5:1 . . . . C15

C14   Body segments, 12 or fewer. The living animal can
      roll into a spherical ball. Widespread throughout
      the British Isles . . . . **Pill millipedes**
                                          GLOMERIDA
                                             (p. 60)

–   More than 12 body segments. The living
      animal can roll up, but not into a spherical
      ball. Restricted to Kent . . . .
                                          Millipedes
                                    POLYZONIIDA
                                             (p. 60)

*Count the number of pairs of legs along one side
of the millipede (1, 2, 3 ... etc.)*

C15   The total number of pairs of legs is an odd
      number . . . . **'Snake' millipedes**
                                             JULIDA
                                             (p. 60)

–   The total number of pairs of legs is an even number
      . . . . **Millipedes**
                                   CHORDEUMATIDA
                            (suborder Chordeumatidea)
                                             (p. 60)

C16   Large pincer-like palps present C17

–   No such palps C18

      Note. Do not confuse pincer palps (d) with the very long
      palps in some spiders. The tips of the latter will not be
      clawed, but will look more like boxing gloves (e).

C17 Abdomen ends in a long tapering 'tail' (the *telson*) (a). Body (not including claws) more than 20 mm long . . . . **Scorpions**
SCORPIONES
(p. 55)

– Abdomen ends abruptly, not in a long tail (b). Body (not including claws) less than 5 mm long
False scorpions
PSEUDOSCORPIONES
(p. 56)

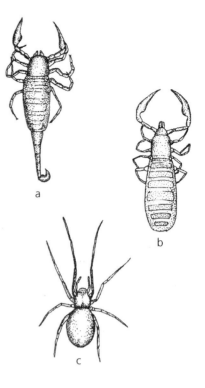

a

b

C18 Head and thorax fused into one and separated from abdomen by a constricted 'waist' – the *pedicel* (c) . . . . **Spiders**
ARANEAE
(p. 56)

Note. The pedicel may not be visible in living animals, but the body is clearly divided into two parts.

c

– Head, thorax and abdomen fused into one – look from above C19

C19 Body clearly segmented – if in doubt look from below. Legs usually more than 1.5 times the length of the body. Body (not including legs) usually larger than 2 mm . . . . **Harvestmen**
OPILIONES
(p. 56)

Note. Segmentation may be difficult to observe in very small individuals. In these cases harvestmen will always have a wart-like projection on the front half of the upper surface (the eye-bearing *ocularium*) (d) which is never present in mites or ticks.

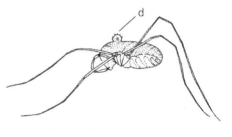

d

– Body apparently not segmented. Legs rarely longer than the body and usually much shorter. Body only larger than 2 mm in a small minority of species . . . . **Mites and ticks**
ACARI
(p. 57)

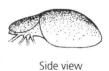

Side view

Top view

KEY D
ANIMALS WITH THREE PAIRS OF JOINTED LEGS. NO WINGS

D1   Animal lives in a tubular *transportable* case (which it carries around with it) constructed of silk, sand grains, hairs, plant material, etc. D2

Note. Beware! Larvae of several groups of insects protect or camouflage themselves with fragments of vegetation, sand, etc. But in most cases this covering does not form a tube. If you can see the under surface of the animal by turning it over without removing the covering, take the second lead, i.e. go to D4.

—   Animal not living in a tubular *transportable* case as above, although it may have a tubular refuge which is fixed to the substrate or vegetation D4

Unfortunately the three groups keying out in D2 and D3 cannot be distinguished on ecological characters alone. You will need to remove the animal, but if you agitate the case or heat it gently in sunshine the animal may emerge without any need to destroy the case.

D2   Abdominal prolegs present (a) . . . . . **Bagworms (larvae of the family Psychidae) LEPIDOPTERA** (p. 73)

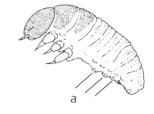

a

—   No abdominal prolegs present D3

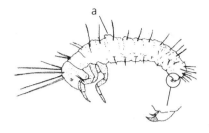

D3   A pair of anal claws present on the rear tip of the abdomen; also, a fleshy lump on the dorsal surface of the 1st abdominal segment (a). Very bristly – some head bristles longer than legs. Mainly in deciduous leaf litter in the Wyre Forest area . . . .
Cased caddis larvae
TRICHOPTERA
(p. 75)

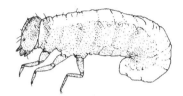

–   No anal claws or dorsal fleshy lump on the abdomen. Not particularly bristly – never with bristles as long as legs. Mainly found in coniferous woods, often associated with ants' nests . . . . .
Cased beetle larvae
COLEOPTERA
(p. 69)

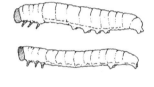

D4   Caterpillar-like. The body is soft and fleshy – often with stumpy abdominal 'prolegs', in addition to the true jointed legs D5

Note. This couplet is included to save time. Don't worry if you are uncertain; difficult groups key out both ways.

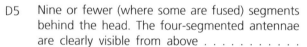

–   Not particularly caterpillar-like D10

D5   Nine or fewer (where some are fused) segments behind the head. The four-segmented antennae are clearly visible from above . . . .
Springtails
COLLEMBOLA
(p. 62)

Note. Recently hatched millipede larvae may be mistaken occasionally for soil-dwelling springtails. These will never be larger than 1.5 mm, usually 0.5 mm or less. They will often have relatively long legs which appear 5-6 segmented, nearly as long as the depth of the abdomen (b). Springtails' legs appear 3-4 segmented and are shorter (c). Millipedes' heads may appear circular or semi-oval in side profile but in springtails the heads are more flattened.

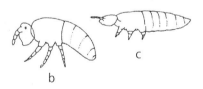

–   More than nine segments behind the head. Antennae comparatively inconspicuous from above, or apparently missing. D6

D6 No abdominal prolegs (see NOTE A, p. 9) D7

– Prolegs present on the abdomen (see NOTE B, p. 9)
. . . . D8

D7 Head oval in side view, with long axis pointing downwards or slightly forwards. Antennae inconspicuous, or apparently absent. Body never covered in hairs. Various colours, but never black throughout. Often found in groups of five or more, sometimes in a 'web' of silky threads . . . .
**Sawfly larvae
HYMENOPTERA
(Suborder Symphyta)**
(p. 71)

– Head flattened in side view, with the long axis pointing forwards. Antennae often obviously present, originating from the front corners of the head (when viewed from above). Various colours, but sometimes black throughout. Usually found individually, rarely in twos and threes, and never in a 'web' of silky threads . . . .
**Beetle larvae
and, rarely, wingless adults**
see D19 note if in doubt
COLEOPTERA
(p. 69)

Note. Very rarely, snow flea larvae (Mecoptera – *Boreus hyemalis*) may key out here. These are found in short moss in sandy areas, are less than 3 mm long, and are usually pale yellowish and have a clearly curved body shape.

D8 4, or fewer, pairs of abdominal prolegs (not including the claspers on the last abdominal segment) . . . . **Larvae of butterflies and moths
LEPIDOPTERA**
(p. 72)

– 5 or more pairs of prolegs (not including those on the last abdominal segment) D9

D9   8 pairs of prolegs (not including those on the last
      abdominal segments) . . . . . **Scorpion fly larvae**
                                          MECOPTERA
                                                (p. 72)

–   5, 6 or 7 pairs of prolegs (not including those on the
      last abdominal segment). Often with a distinctive
      black spot on their head capsule . . . .
                                          Sawfly larvae
                                      (Suborder Symphyta)
                                          HYMENOPTERA
                                                (p. 71)

      Note. Some moth larvae may key out here. These will
      be very small, less than 5 mm, and associated with
      moss. They are also distinguished by having hooks on
      the ends of their prolegs, which are never present in
      sawfly or scorpion fly larvae.

D10   Antennae not present (or strongly reduced and
      thus apparently absent) D11

–   Antennae present D16

D11   Abdomen not segmented, and apparently
      fused to the thorax. Body length less than
      1 mm . . . . **Mite larvae**
                                                ACARI
                                                (p. 57)

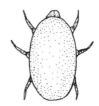

–   Abdomen segmented. Body length often larger
      than 1 mm, usually much larger D12

D12   Legs not easily seen; often hidden under the body.
      Clings to plant surface . . . **Female scale insects**
                                 HEMIPTERA (Family Coccoidea)
                                                (p. 66)

      Note. Scale insects are a difficult group to identify. The
      insect is covered in a waxy scale which has to be lifted
      off before the animal can be seen. They also lack clear
      external features and have a wide variety of shapes,
      some of which are illustrated in Fig. 3 overleaf.

–   Legs easily seen. Animal can be fully mobile, not
      clinging to plant surface D13

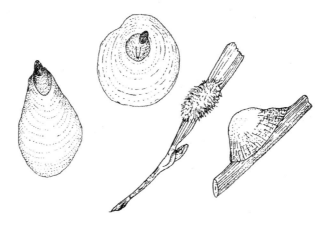

Figure 3. A range of scale insects – actual animals up to 3 mm long. (After Green, 1922).

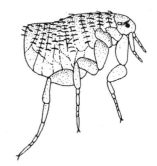

D13 Body laterally compressed – flattened from side-
     to-side. Never more than 9 mm long . . . . **Fleas**
                                            SIPHONAPTERA
                                                 (p. 74)

–   Body not laterally compressed D14

D14 Free living. Abdomen elongate, length more
     than twice the width (look from above). Not
     particularly flattened from top-to-bottom (dorso-
     ventrally) D15

–   External parasites, mainly on vertebrates
     but may be found off their host. Abdomen
     short, its length rarely more than twice the
     width (look from above), and often flattened
     from top-to-bottom D52

D15 Head pointed in front to give the animal a characteristic 'torpedo' shape (a). Front legs held forward, like a pair of 'feelers'. Body length less than 2 mm . . . . : **PROTURA** (p. 62)

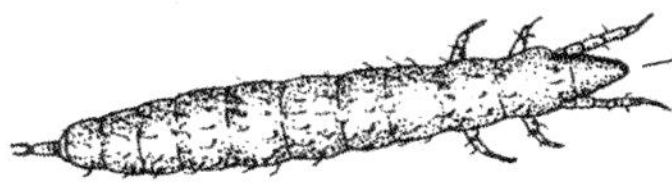

a

 –   Head not tapering in front to give torpedo shape. Usually larger than 2 mm . . . . **Beetle larvae COLEOPTERA** (p. 69)

D16 Each antenna is clearly branched (bifurcate), and the branches extend at least half the length of the antenna. Whole animal smaller than 1 mm . . . . **Larval PAUROPODA** (p. 60)

 –   Antennae unbranched, or only slightly branched (i.e. near the tip of the antennae). Whole animal usually larger than 1 mm, but not always D17

D17 Mouthparts formed into a segmented sucking tube which is held under the body, pointing downwards or backwards. Mouthparts without segmented palps . . . . **Bugs HEMIPTERA** (p. 67)

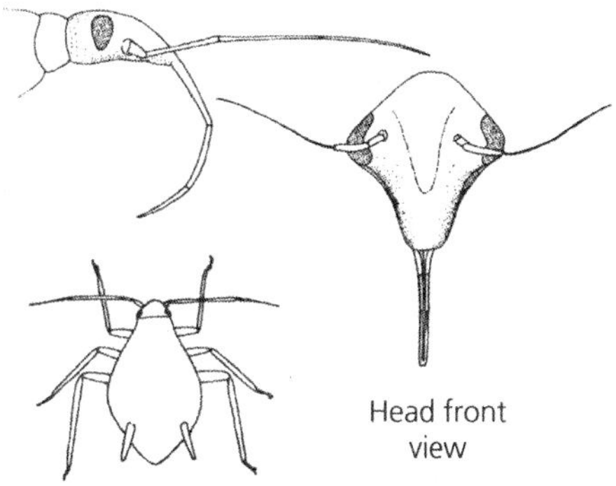

Head side view

Note. Very rarely, Anoplura (sucking lice), wingless Diptera and Lepidoptera could cause problems here. The lice are easily distinguished by their short and stout legs (shorter than the width of the abdomen), with a single tarsal segment terminating in a single large claw. Diptera and Lepidoptera will have five (or apparently four) tarsal segments (Hemiptera have a maximum of three), and may have segmented palpal mouthparts also.

Head front view

Top view

 –   Mouthparts don't form a tube which is held under the body. *If uncertain look for segmented palps; if these are present choose this lead* D18

D18 The pronotum (the upper part of the first thoracic segment) extends over the head to form a shield-like covering when the animal is viewed from above (a) D19

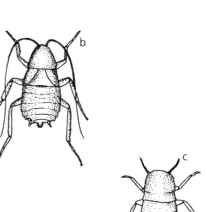

–   Most of the dorsal surface of the head visible D20

D19 Antennae very long – nearly as long as, or longer than, the body. Many more than 11 antennal segments (b) . . . . **Cockroaches DICTYOPTERA** (p. 65)

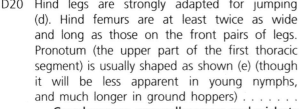

–   Antennae relatively short – never longer than the width of the pronotum. Up to 11 antennal segments (c) . . . . **Beetle larvae (and, rarely, wingless adults) COLEOPTERA** (p. 69)

Note. Adult beetles will have 5 tarsal segments on each leg, and 11 antennal segments. Larvae will not have this combination.

D20 Hind legs are strongly adapted for jumping (d). Hind femurs are at least twice as wide and long as those on the front pairs of legs. Pronotum (the upper part of the first thoracic segment) is usually shaped as shown (e) (though it will be less apparent in young nymphs, and much longer in ground hoppers) . . . . **Grasshoppers, groundhoppers and crickets ORTHOPTERA** (p. 66)

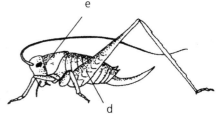

–   Without this combination of leg and pronotum features D21

D21 2 or 3 'tails' or projecting appendages (cerci) on terminal segments of the abdomen D22

Note. Beware of broken tails. Most animals are symmetrical; if a tail on one side is not complemented by a similar appendage on the other look for a remnant – a stub, a broken base, etc.

– Terminal 'tails' absent or very short, or only one (though this may divide towards the tip) D32

D22 3 abdominal appendages present D23

– 2 abdominal appendages present D24

Note. Beware of breakages.

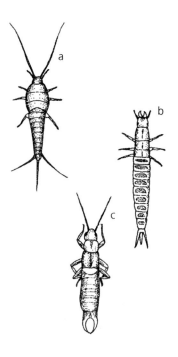

D23 Antennae long, at least 1.5 times the width of the head (a). Body carrot-shaped; becoming narrower from front to back . . . . **Three-pronged bristletails ARCHEAOGNATHA (p. 63)**

– Antennae short, less than 1.5 times the width of the head (b). Body rarely carrot-shaped . . . **Beetle larvae COLEOPTERA (p. 69)**

D24 Abdominal appendages are strong and curved inwards (c) . . . . **Earwigs DERMAPTERA (p. 65)**

– Abdominal appendages not as broad, and not curved, or only slightly so D25

D25 Abdominal appendages are long and thin, at least one quarter the length of the abdomen D26

– Appendages are shorter than one quarter the length of the abdomen D29

D26 Look from above. Abdominal appendages converge, or are parallel, or diverge only slightly so that the distance between the tips is never greater than the width of the abdomen (a) D27

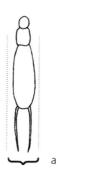
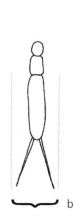

Note. In marginal cases – if the appendages have bristles longer than the diameter of the 'tail', choose the second lead, i.e. go to D28. If they don't have bristles, or have bristles which are narrower than the width of the tail, choose the first lead; i.e. go to D27.

–   Abdominal appendages diverge from their base so that the distance between their tips is greater than the width of the abdomen when viewed from above (b) D28

D27 Nine or fewer body segments behind the head. Antennae four- or six-segmented. Abdominal appendages are joined at, or near, the base. Often with a wart-like tube under the abdomen, between, or just behind, the hind legs . . . . . .
Springtails
COLLEMBOLA
(p. 62)

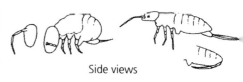
Side views

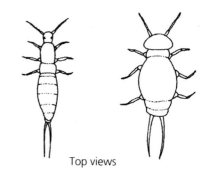
Top views

Note. Rarely, 'secondary' segmentation of the antennae may cause problems. In these cases the antennae have surface grooves which may look like the joins between true segments and could give the impression that there are more than the 'true' number of segments. However, the number of body segments, the 'tail' and the wart-like tube will be sufficient for identification.

–   More than nine body segments behind the head. Eight or more antennal segments. Abdominal appendages are clearly separate at their bases and originate from the outward hind corners of the abdomen. Never with a wart-like tube under the body . . . . **Earwig nymphs**
DERMAPTERA
(p. 65)

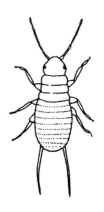

D28 Long antennae – at least 2.5 times as long as the width of the head (a). Animal less than 5 mm long. 'Tails' are composed of many segments . . . **Two-pronged bristle tails**
DIPLURA
(p. 62)

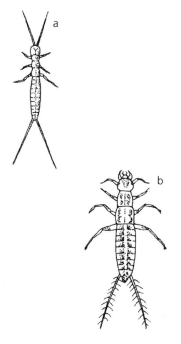

Note. Occasionally, springtails (Collembola) and some adult stoneflies (Plecoptera) with vestigial wings may key out here. In the springtails, the antennae never have more than four segments and the body behind the head is clearly nine-segmented. The stoneflies are usually found near running water, are dark-coloured, have compound eyes and three tarsal segments per leg. In contrast, bristletails are widespread, are pale-coloured, have no compound eyes and only one tarsal segment per leg.

– Antennae are never longer than twice the width of the head (b). Often larger than 5 mm. 'Tails' unsegmented, or consisting of less than 5 segments . . . . **Beetle larvae**
COLEOPTERA
(p. 69)

D29 Abdominal appendages are short, located forward of the tip of the abdomen and above the lateral mid-line **D30**

– Not as above **D31**

Head side view

Head front view

D30 Mouthparts forming a sucking tube (look under the head, and also between the bases of the front legs). No segmented palps . . . . **Bugs**
HEMIPTERA
(p. 67)

– Biting mouthparts, or no obvious tube-like structure. Segmented palps present . . . .
Beetle larvae
COLEOPTERA
(p. 69)

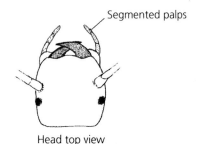

Segmented palps

Head top view

D31 Antennae approximately twice as long as
     the width of the head; long, piercing
     mouthparts (a) . . . . **Lacewings**
                                      NEUROPTERA
                                          (p. 74)

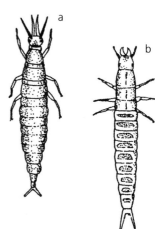

–   Antennae usually shorter than 2 times the
     width of the head; biting mouthparts (b) . . . .
                                    Beetle larvae
                                      COLEOPTERA
                                          (p. 70)

Top view

D32 The body is sharply constricted into a
     waist between the abdomen and the thorax
     (look carefully; if you are unsure look from the
     side as well as from above) . . . .
                                Apterous (wingless)
                                Bees, ants and wasps
                                (Suborder Apocrita)
                                      HYMENOPTERA
                                          (p. 71)

     Note. Booklice (Psocoptera) may key out here. These
     always have two- or three- segmented tarsi and are
     rarely longer than 3 mm. (Hymenoptera nearly always
     have 5).

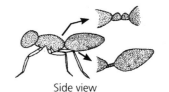

Side view

–   No sharply constricted 'waist' between the
     abdomen and thorax D33

D33 Ten, or more, antennal segments D34

–   Less than ten antennal segments D42

     Note. The antennal segmentation may be difficult to
     see in smaller specimens. These specimens should
     key out both ways, but check nevertheless by keying
     through both sections. Also, beware of breakages. If
     one antenna is obviously longer than the other count
     the number of segments on the former. If in doubt, key
     both ways and you will probably find that you arrive at
     the same answer anyway.

D34 Body is clothed in a dense covering of scales (which may appear as hairs) . . . .
Wingless female moths
LEPIDOPTERA
(p. 73)

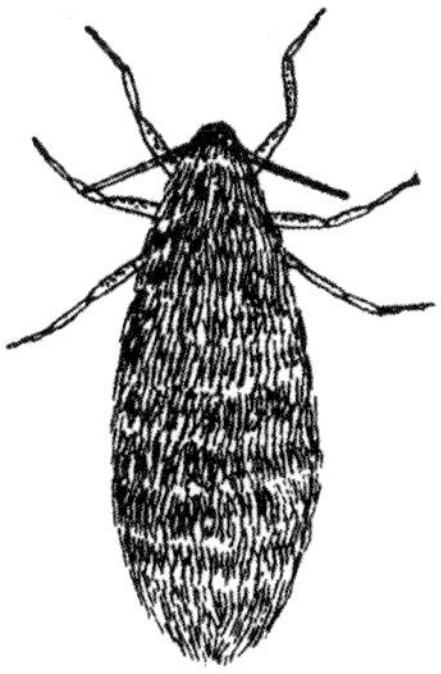

– Body not densely clothed in scales or hairs . . . D35

D35 Body is unusually long and thin, at least eight times longer than broad . . . .
Stick insects
PHASMIDA
(p. 67)

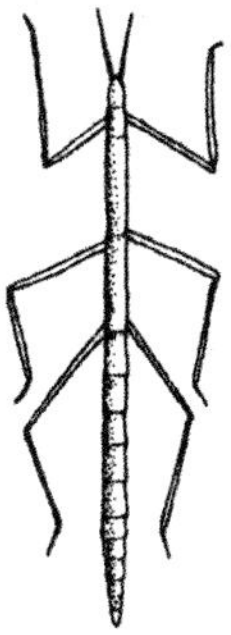

– Body not particularly long and thin D36

D36 Head is extended downwards, forming an obvious 'beak' (a) . . . . **Snow fleas**
MECOPTERA
(p. 72)

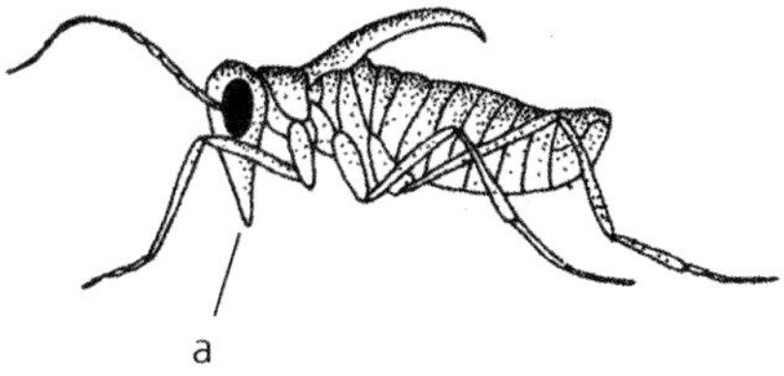

– Head not forming a 'beak' D37

a

D37 Long antennae (beware of broken antennae), their length at least 2 times the width of the head D38

– Antennae no more than 1.5 times as long as the width of the head D40

b

D38 Rudimentary wings present on the side of the thorax (look closely, b). Body larger than 7 mm
'Wingless' adult female caddis flies
TRICHOPTERA
(p. 75)

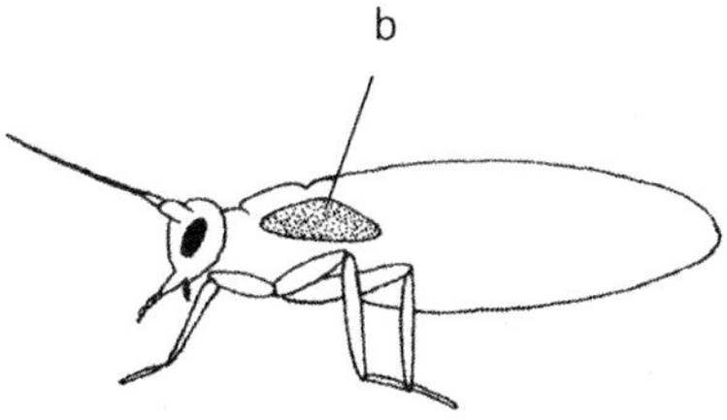

– No rudimentary wings on the side of the thorax. Body, often (but not always) smaller than 5 mm
. . . . D39

D39   The main body (thorax and abdomen) has a
      fusiform (i.e. tapered at both ends) or oval
      shape (look from above). Large piercing jaws
      (a), or club-shaped mouthparts (b), project in
      front of the head. Sometimes larger than 5 mm
                               Lacewing larvae
                                  NEUROPTERA
                                      (p. 74)

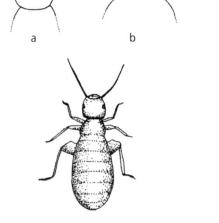

—   At least partly 'waisted' between thorax and
      abdomen, thus not forming a fusiform or oval
      shape. Never have large piercing jaws, or club-
      shaped mouthparts, projecting in front of the
      head. Always less than 5 mm long . . . .
                                      Booklice
                                  PSOCOPTERA
                                      (p. 69)

D40   Tarsi   of   the   legs   are   five-segmented.
      Antennae 11-segmented. Jaws are not visible
      from above (c, d) . . . .
                         Wingless adult beetles
                                  COLEOPTERA
                                      (p. 69)

      Note. Sometimes, 'winged' beetles may key out here,
      in which case you have missed the short wing cases (e)
      – see NOTE B, p. 9.

—   Either the tarsi are not five-segmented, or the
      antennae have fewer than 11 segments. Jaws are
      visible from above (f, g) D41

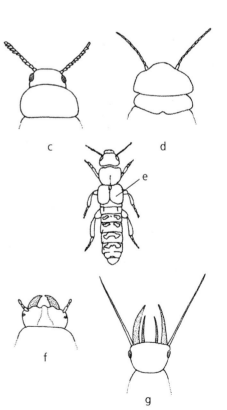

D41 Antennae thread-like (with the segmentation difficult to see), at least as long as the width of the head, but often much longer. Jaws long and projecting well in front of the head (look from above) (a). Body usually broadest towards the middle, and tapering towards the ends (b) . . . . **Lacewing larvae**
NEUROPTERA
(p. 73)

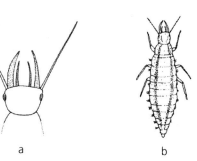

a   b

–   Antennae stout, clearly segmented, and often shorter than the width of the head. Jaws strongly curved and usually folded in front of the head so that they overlap (c). Abdomen often parallel-sided, or broadest at the front end (d) .
. . . . **Beetle larvae**
COLEOPTERA
(p. 69)

c

d

D42 Legs indistinct, often hidden under the body. Clings to plant surface. See Figure 3, p. 26 . . . . **Female scale insects**
HEMIPTERA
(p. 67)

Note. Scale insects are a difficult group to identify. The insect is covered in a waxy scale which has to be lifted off before the body can be seen. They often lack clear external features and have a wide variety of shapes, some of which are illustrated on p. 26.

–   Legs easily seen. Animal is freely mobile, and not firmly attached to the surface of a plant
. . . . D43

D43   Nine body segments behind the head, with a
      bilobed wart-like tube under the first abdominal
      segment (you may have to tease the hind
      set of legs apart to see this). Usually with a
      springing organ trailing behind the abdomen or
      tucked underneath . . . . **Springtails**
                                    COLLEMBOLA
                                          (p. 62)

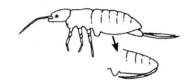

      Note. In some springtails (Collembola) the springing
      organ is missing, but the ventral tube is usually present.
      Minute, recently hatched millipede larvae may be
      mistaken for soil-dwelling springtails. See note under
      D5.

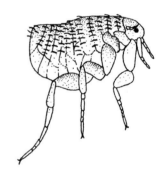

–   More than nine body segments behind the head,
      with no springing organ D44

D44   Body laterally compressed – looks as if it has
      been squashed from side-to-side . . . . **Fleas**
                                    SIPHONAPTERA
                                          (p. 74)

–   Body is not obviously laterally compressed . . . D45

D45   The upper surface of the head and the first
      segment of the thorax – the prothorax (a) – are
      hardened and shiny, and clearly very different
      from the other two thoracic segments (b).
      The prothorax is very elongated, at least 1.5
      times as long as the next thoracic segment
      (the mesothorax) . . . .
                          Snakefly larvae and pupae
                                    RAPHIDIOPTERA
                                          (p. 74)

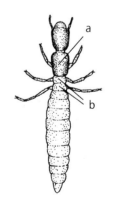

–   The prothorax is no more hardened or shiny
      than the following two thoracic segments;
      usually not obviously extended D46

D46 Strong jaws projecting in front of the head (when viewed from above (a, b) – these may appear as two individual stylets D41

– Jaws do not clearly project in front of the head, and where the mouthparts have been adapted into a tube-like structure, this is always held underneath the body, pointing backwards D47

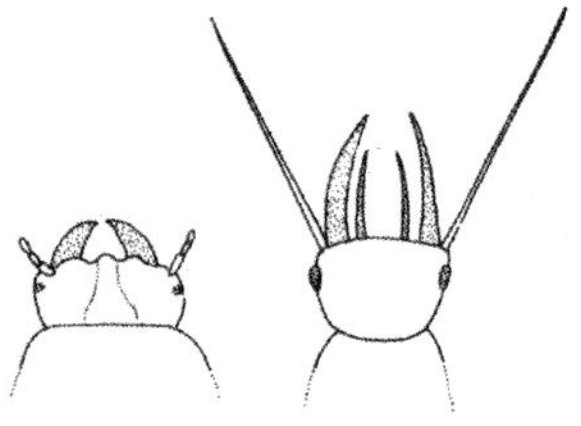

a   b

D47 The head is narrow, less than one third of the maximum body width (look from above) . . .
Sucking lice
PHTHIRAPTERA
(p. 68)

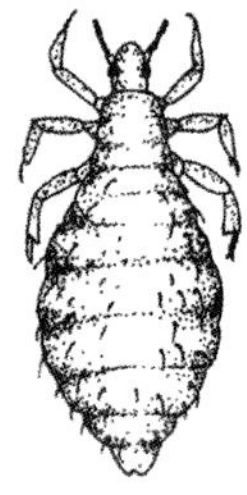

– The head is not narrow, its width being greater than one third of the maximum body width (look from above) D48

D48 Mouthparts forming a segmented rigid tube, which is held under the body pointing downwards or backwards. Without segmented palps . . . . **Apterous (wingless)**
Adult and nymphal bugs
HEMIPTERA
(p. 67)

Side view

– Mouthparts not forming a tube, and often with segmented palps D49

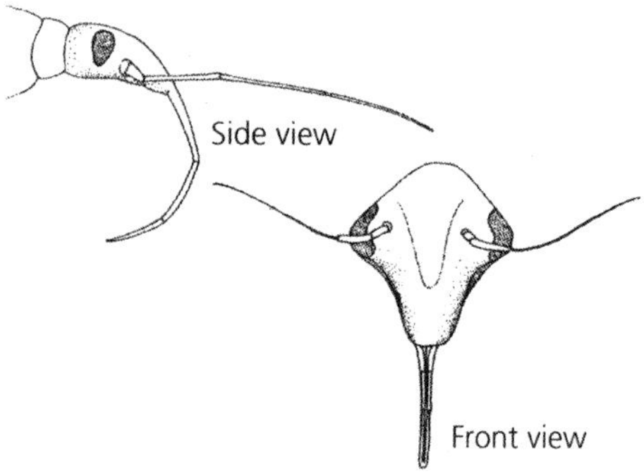

Front view

D49 Distinct antennae – as long as, or longer than, the width of the head D50

– Antennae very inconspicuous – length less than the width of the head D51

D50   More than nine antennal segments (although
       these may be difficult to see). Each antenna
       consists of two large basal segments followed
       by a flagellum of 11-20 or more segments.
       Head relatively large, its length at least 1/4
       the length of the rest of the body. The body
       often appears pale and almost translucent
       with background lighting . . . . **Booklice**
       PSOCOPTERA
       (p. 69)

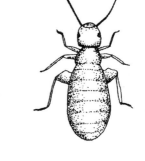

 –   Nine, or fewer, antennal segments. Antennae
       never consisting of two larger basal segments
       followed by a flagellum. Head relatively small, its
       length rarely exceeding more than one quarter
       the length of the rest of the body. Body not
       translucent with background lighting . . . **Thrips**
       THYSANOPTERA
       (p. 69)

       Note. Very rarely, wingless adult Diptera may key out
       through both leads above. These will have five tarsal
       segments, whereas booklice and thrips will have a
       maximum of three.

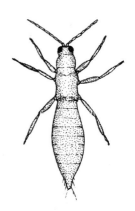

D51   Various sizes, often larger than 6 mm. Where
       smaller than 6 mm abdomen widest in the front
       quarter of its length, either tapering towards the
       back end, or parallel-sided for most of its length
       and tapering in the last quarter . . . **Beetle larvae**
       COLEOPTERA
       (p. 69)

 –   Smaller than 6 mm. Abdomen not as above. Either
       almost oval (from above), or widest towards the
       middle of its length and tapering towards each
       end. Often associated with birds and mammals
       (also, sometimes bees), either as external parasites,
       or through phoresis ('hitching a lift') D52

D52 Obvious 'neck' present between the head and
     the thorax. Tarsi one- or two- segmented . . . .
                                    Biting lice
                               PHTHIRAPTERA
                                      (p. 68)

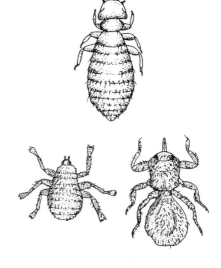

–   No distinct neck present – the head often sunk
     into the thorax. Tarsi five-segmented. Mainly
     associated with birds and mammals (particularly
     bats), but also found on bees . . . . . . **True flies**
                                    DIPTERA
                                     (p. 70)

KEY E
ANIMALS WITH THREE PAIRS OF JOINTED LEGS. ONE PAIR OF WINGS

E1   Abdomen terminating in 'tails', or clumps of bristles E2

–   No appendages on the tip of the abdomen E4

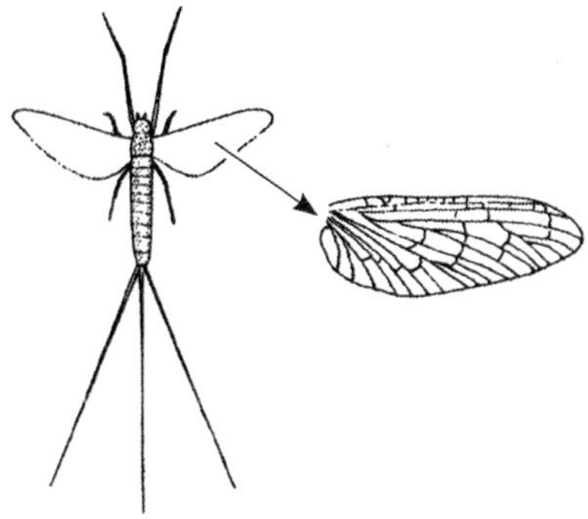

E2   Two or three long 'tails' present, and these are longer than the length of the abdomen (beware of breakages). Complex wing venation; many 'closed' cells. Antennae shorter than the width of the head . . . . **Mayflies**
EPHEMEROPTERA
(p. 64)

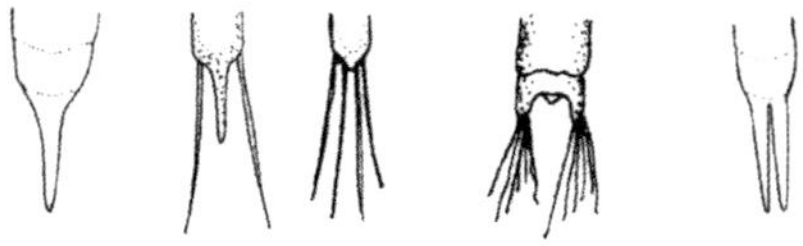

–   Abdomen terminating in one (a), two (b) or four (c) tapering 'tails', or a pair of appendages which may (d), or may not (e), be adorned with a clump of bristles, but are never longer than the abdomen. Simple wing venation, with or without 'closed' cells. Antennae usually longer than the width of the head, although only occasionally it may be shorter E3

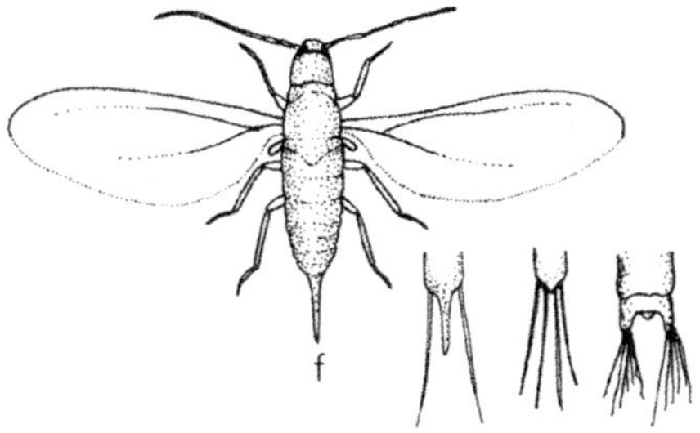

a   b   c   d   e

E3   Abdomen terminating in one (f), two (g) or four (h) tapering 'tails', or paired clumps of bristles (i). Simple wing venation; no closed cells and less than three veins reaching the outer wing margin. Body less than 1.5 mm long. One tarsal segment per leg . . . .
Male scale insects
HEMIPTERA
(Family Coccoidea)
(p. 67)

–   Abdomen terminating with a narrow pair of appendages which do not end in two clumps of bristles. Five or more veins reaching the outer wing margin. Body often larger than 1.5 mm. Five tarsal segments per leg . . . .
True flies
DIPTERA
(p. 70)

f

g   h   i

E4 Club-like balancers (halteres) in front of the wings. Wings as broad as, or broader than, long (a). Body less than 3 mm long. Distinctive antennae (b) . . . .
STREPSIPTERA
(p. 74)

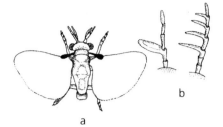

– Halteres located behind the wings (c, d). Wings are never as broad as long. Body often larger than 3 mm. Antennae usually simple (e) . . . **True flies DIPTERA**
(p. 70)

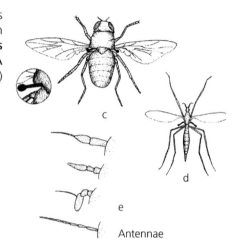

Antennae

Note. Halteres may sometimes be hidden by a membranous flap (f). Don't worry; in these cases the antennal characters will separate these two groups.

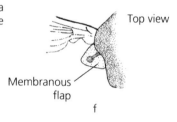

Top view

Membranous flap

f

IF YOUR SPECIMEN DOES NOT KEY OUT HERE GO TO **KEY F.** YOU HAVE MISSED A PAIR OF WINGS, OR YOUR SPECIMEN'S HIND WINGS HAVEN'T DEVELOPED YET.

KEY F
ANIMALS WITH THREE PAIRS OF JOINTED LEGS. TWO PAIRS OF WINGS

F1   Animal covered in a white powdery dust or wax
      . . . . F2

      Note. Do not confuse pale hairs with dust or wax. If in doubt, go to F3.

—   Animal not covered in white dust or wax
      . . . . F3

F2   Wings held roof-like over the body. Simple venation in the forewings, with fewer than four veins reaching the wing margin (although these may not be very obvious) . . . **Whiteflies HEMIPTERA**
      (p. 67)

—   Wings not held roof-like over body. Wing venation quite complex, with at least eight veins reaching the margin of the forewings . . .
      NEUROPTERA
      (Family Coniopterygidae)
      (p. 73)

F3   The front wings form hardened or leathery covers (the *elytra*; see NOTE B, p. 9) under which the fully membranous hind wings are usually withdrawn and hidden. Venation is missing completely from the elytra (though there may be a surface pattern: ridges, grooves, pits, etc.). Remember, the elytra may be very short and extend only part-way down the abdomen . . . F4

—   Front wings do not form elytra. Both sets of wings are completely or partly membranous, with varying amounts of venation (but the veins may be covered in scales or hairs); or both sets of wings may appear as strap-like pads
      . . . . F7

F4   Two long, strongly curved (pincer-like) abdominal
      tails (cerci) (a) . . . . Earwigs
                                        DERMAPTERA
                                              (p. 65)

–   No pincer-like cerci F5

F5   Antennae apparently absent or, if present,
      consisting of twelve or less antennal segments (look
      carefully – some antennae may appear long but only
      have three or four segments). The antennae are
      usually 'simple' or 'threadlike' (a), but *sometimes*
      may have an obvious 'club' at the end (c) . . . F6

–   Antennae consisting of more than twelve
      segments; *never* with a large 'club' F14

      Note. Antennal segmentation can be difficult to see.
      Don't worry, awkward groups should key out both
      ways but check anyway if in doubt. Also, beware of
      breakages; if one antenna is longer than the other count
      the segmentation of the longer one.

F6   Mouthparts forming a segmented tube (a, b). This
      may be short, in which case the 'beak' gives the
      head profile a characteristic triangular shape when
      viewed from in front (c). The beak may be carried
      curved backwards (reflexed) under the body.
      Mouth parts lack segmented palps . . . . **Bugs**
                                           HEMIPTERA
                                              (p. 67)

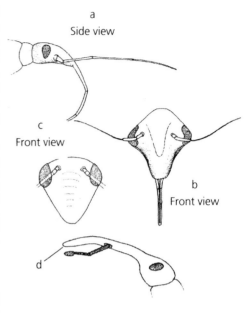

a
Side view

c
Front view

b
Front view

d

      Note. Some beetles, particularly weevils (family
      Curculionidae) may have the head extended into a long
      snout – the rostrum (d). This usually points forwards, but
      may sometimes be curved under the body. These can be
      separated from the bugs by the presence of elbowed
      antennae which arises some way along the rostrum.
      Also, the forelegs of beetles will have four or five tarsal
      segments, the bugs will have a maximum of three.

–   Biting mouthparts. Mouthparts include segmented
      palps . . . . **Beetles**
                                          COLEOPTERA
                                              (p. 69)

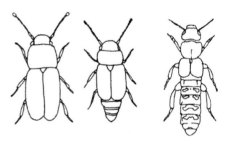

F7   The two pairs of wings are strap-shaped or form
      blunt stubs, with (f) or without (e) a fringe of
      long hairs and lacking obvious venation F8

–   The wings are not strap-shaped; they are usually
      fully membranous, with venation, but this may be
      covered in scales and/or hairs F10

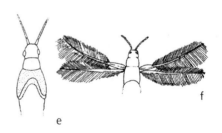

f

e

F8   Wings are fringed with long hairs . . . .
                                              Thrips
                                        THYSANOPTERA
                                              (p. 69)

–   Wings are not fringed with hairs F9

F9   Mouthparts forming a segmented tube (a).
      No segmented palps. The tube may be short
      in which case the head profile will be a
      characteristic triangular shape when viewed
      from in front (b). No segmented palps . . . . .
      . . . . **Nymphal and brachypterous**
      (Short-winged) adult bugs
      HEMIPTERA
      (p. 68)

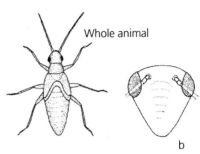

−   Biting mouth parts; no tube-like structure.
      Segmented palps present. Head never triangular
      in profile (c) . . . .
      nymphal and brachypterous
      (short-winged) adult Bugs
      PSOCOPTERA
      (p. 69)

F10   Antennae apparently absent, or with fewer
      than nine segments F11

−   Nine or more antennal segments F14

F11   Two or three long abdominal 'tails' . . . .
      Mayflies
      EMPHEMEROPTERA
      (p. 64)

−   No such tails (beware of breakages) F12

F12   Animal more than 21 mm long (*measure the animal; this is a critical couplet*) . . . .
Dragonflies and damselflies
ODONATA
(p. 64)

–   Animal less than 20 mm long (*measure the animal; this is a critical couplet*) F13

Whole animals

F13   Mouthparts forming a segmented tube (a, b). This may be short, thus forming a 'beak' which gives the head profile a characteristic triangular shape when viewed from in front (c). No segmented palps . . . . **Bugs**
HEMIPTERA
(p. 67)

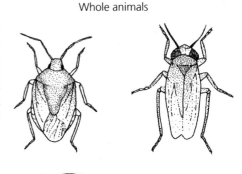

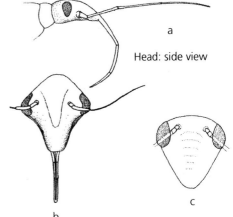

a
Head: side view

b
Head: front view

c
Head: front view

–   Biting mouthparts. Segmented palps usually present F14

F14 Pronotum (the upper plate of the first thoracic segment) well developed, either saddle shaped (a), or extending forwards to cover much of the head (b) F15

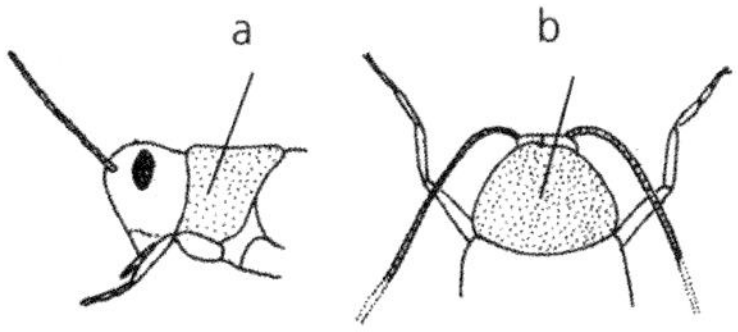

– Pronotum not as described and illustrated above F16

F15 Hind legs modified for jumping, with greatly enlarged femora (c). Head not covered by the pronotum (d) . . . .
**Grasshoppers, crickets and groundhoppers
ORTHOPTERA**
(p. 66)

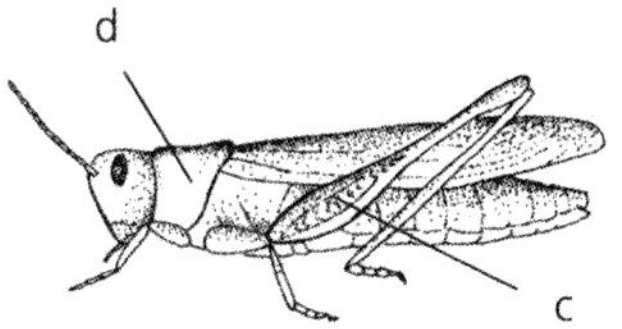

– Hind legs not modified for jumping. When seen from above, the head is largely covered by the pronotal shield (e) . . . **Cockroaches
DICTYOPTERA**
(p. 65)

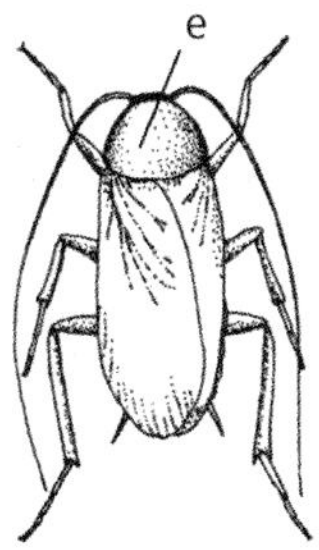

F16 With a sharply constricted 'waist' between the thorax and the abdomen; look from the side if you are unsure. Wings never covered in scales, though they may have short hairs F17

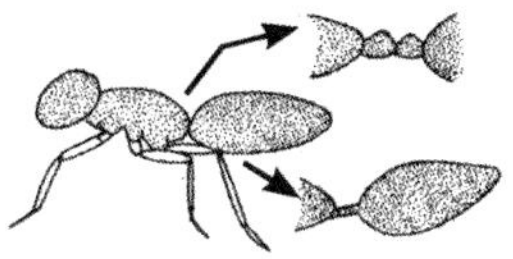

– Without a waist between the thorax and the abdomen F18

F17 Tarsi are four- or five-segmented. Wings never held roof-like over the body (f, g) . . . . . .
**Bees, ants and wasps
HYMENOPTERA (Apocrita)**
(p. 71)

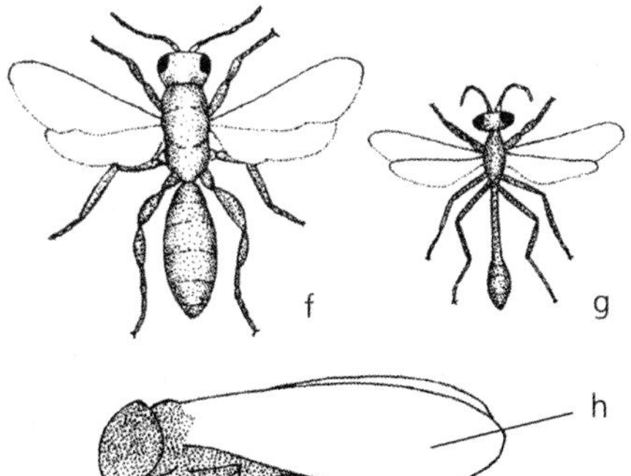

– Tarsi are two- or three- segmented. Wings held roof-like over the body (h) F27

F18 Two long abdominal 'tails' (cerci). Beware
     of breakages . . . . **Stoneflies**
                                          PLECOPTERA
                                              (p. 67)

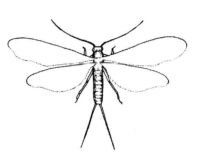

–   Without two long cerci F19

F19 Wings densely covered in scales or obvious hairs
     between the veins (as well as on them); often
     with reduced venation, i.e. only a few cross veins.
     These features may be easier to see with lighting
     from underneath F20

–   Clear wing venation. Wings not covered in
     scales or hairs (though veins may appear 'hairy')
     . . . . F21

     Note. If there are short hairs sparsely distributed
     between veins, but no fringe of hairs around the wing
     margin, then go to couplet F21.

F20 Wings covered in scales and often clearly
     patterned. Mouthparts usually modified into a
     proboscis which may be coiled under the body
     (a). LOOK CLOSELY: the scales may be difficult
     to see except under high magnification. Try
     gently rubbing a small section of the wing with
     your fingers or a paintbrush to dislodge some
     scales . . . . **Moths and butterflies**
                                          LEPIDOPTERA
                                              (p. 72)

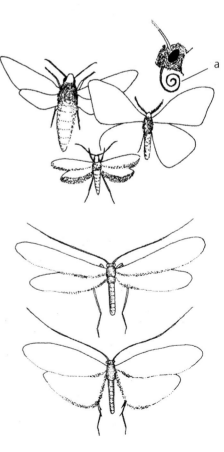

–   Wings are hairy, but not covered in scales.
     Although the wings may be pigmented, they
     are rarely strikingly patterned. Mouthparts
     never form a proboscis (but may have long,
     hairy segmented palps) . . . . **Caddis flies**
                                          TRICHOPTERA
                                              (p.75)

     Note. These two groups can be difficult to separate
     in some cases; if in doubt examine the wings under a
     microscope – all moths are covered in scales, though
     these may be reduced in the more primitive groups.

F21 Face forming a long downward pointed 'beak' (a); the abdomen of adult males forms a sting-like tail (which is harmless) (b) . . . . **Scorpion flies MECOPTERA** (p. 72)

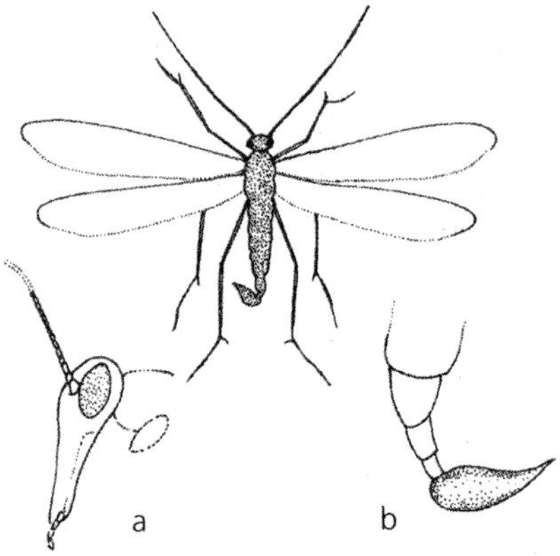

a   b

– Head not particularly extended, not forming a downward pointing 'beak'. Abdomen never terminating with a 'sting-like' tail F22

F22 Front wings with a series of parallel veins running towards their leading edges . . . F23

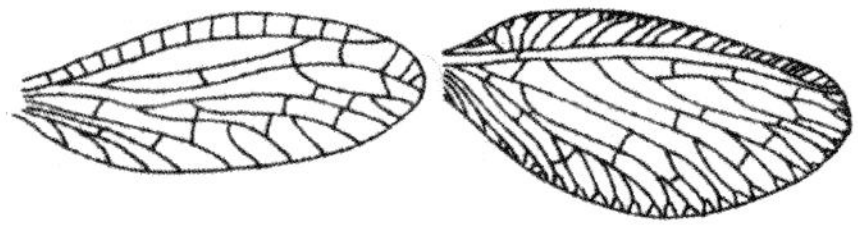

– Front wings lacking a series of parallel veins running towards their leading edges . . . F25

F23 The front part of the body is elongated, with the combined length of the extended head and first thoracic segment (c) (the prothorax – which does not bear wings) being at least 1.5 times the length of the other two thoracic segments (the mesothorax and metathorax) together (d) . . . . **Snakeflies RAPHIDIOPTERA** (p. 74)

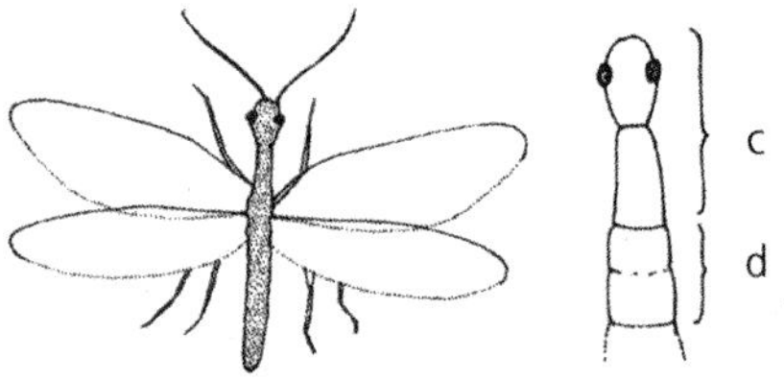

c
d

– The front part of the body is not particularly elongated, with the length of the head and prothorax (e) being equal to, or shorter than, the combined length of the hindmost two thoracic segments (f) F24

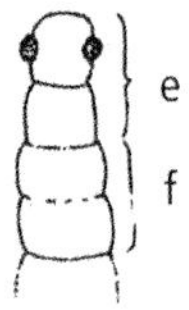

e
f

F24   The outer veins fork before the edges of
      the wing margins. The prothorax (see F23)
      is distinctly narrower than the other thoracic
      segments and the head (including the
      eyes) . . . . **Lacewings**
                                      NEUROPTERA
                                          (p. 73)

–   The hind edge veins do not fork. The
      prothorax is wide and forms a continuous
      outline with the head . . . . **Alderflies**
                                      MEGALOPTERA
                                          (p. 73)

F25   Complex wing venation (a). More than five
      'closed' cells in the forewings (see Fig. 1,
      p. 4) F26

–   Reduced wing venation (b). Never with more
      than three, usually only one, 'closed' cells
      in forewings (see Fig. 1, p. 4) F27

F26   Tarsi three-segmented (or apparently two-
      segmented). Front wings never with a pigmented
      stigma on the front edge. Antennae often
      with more than 20 segments . . . . . **Stoneflies**
                                      PLECOPTERA
                                          (p. 67)

–   Tarsi five-segmented. Often with a pigmented
      stigma on the front edge of the forewings,
      and the antennae with less than 20 segments
                                          Sawflies
                                      HYMENOPTERA
                                  (Suborder Symphyta)
                                          (p. 72)

F27   Antennae clothed in fine hairs throughout. There is a distinct 'neck' between the head and the thorax. The upper surface of the thorax and/or abdomen lacks a striking banding pattern . . . .
Booklice
PSOCOPTERA
(p. 69)

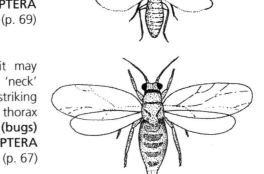

–   Antennae without fine hairs although it may have some hairs at the tip. No distinct 'neck' between head and thorax. Often with a striking dark/pale banding pattern on the upper thorax and/or abdomen . . . . . . **Plant lice (bugs)**
HEMIPTERA
(p. 67)

Taxonomy

No single text deals with all the invertebrate groups likely to be encountered in British terrestrial habitats. However, the following three books will provide a useful introduction. Wheater & Cook (2003) is an introduction to the study of invertebrates. Barnard (2011) and Chinery (2012) provide comprehensive guides to the insects. Many other texts deal with invertebrate groups but are restricted, either in the groups included, in the habitats covered or in the accompanying information provided.

The animal kingdom is divided into a number of major groups known as phyla (singular phylum). These are the largest taxonomic groupings and are themselves split up into increasingly smaller taxa as follows:

Phylum – Class – Order – Family – Genus – Species

Each of these groups may sometimes be further divided into sub-groups. There is some disagreement regarding the number of invertebrate phyla, but most biologists agree that there are between 10 and 15. Of these, several live exclusively in marine and/or freshwater aquatic environments, whilst some are restricted to terrestrial habitats outside Britain, usually in the tropics. None of these is included in this guide. Representatives of eight phyla of macroscopic invertebrates are likely to be found in British terrestrial habitats and these are listed below, with the taxonomic sub-groups that are involved.

The taxonomy outlined here has been updated in 2014. Unless otherwise indicated, where a number of species is given for a particular taxon, it includes both Great Britain and Ireland.

Phylum NEMATODA (Eelworms)

The eelworms are non-segmented and cylindrical. Most are less than 1 mm in length but one common species can reach 200 mm. Identification is extremely difficult and is best left to experts. They were formerly a Class within the now-obsolete Phylum Aschelminthes.

Ecology: The number of species is unknown, but possibly many hundreds. Nematodes are extremely widespread and complex, and include parasitic and free-living forms, with a large number alternating between both lifestyles. Many are carnivorous, whilst others feed exclusively on plant juices and bacteria. Most free-living forms are restricted to the soil but the largest British nematode, *Mermis nigrescens*, can be found climbing vegetation on moist spring and summer days. These are egg-laying females. The eggs are ingested by plant-eating insects and the hatched young parasitise these hosts which are killed eventually. Maturation is completed in the soil and the life-cycle begins again. By encysting, many nematodes have the ability to suspend their development and remain dormant for long periods in unfavourable conditions. Cysts have remained viable for 15 years in this state.

Further reading: Cloudsley-Thompson & Sankey (1961), Kevan (1962), Goodey (1963), and Jackson & Raw (1966).

Phylum NEMATOMORPHA (Hairworms)

The hairworms are non-segmented and cylindrical. They can reach lengths of 300 mm and may be more darkly pigmented than nematodes. They were formerly a Class within the now-obsolete Phylum Aschelminthes.

Ecology: The young parasitise insects, but the adults are free-living in freshwater and in adjacent damp soils. They tend to be restricted to damp soil or thick vegetation in close proximity to freshwater. Four British species.

Further reading: Cloudsley-Thompson & Sankey (1961), Kevan (1962), Goodey (1963) and Jackson & Raw (1966).

Phylum PLATYHELMINTHES

Generally flattened worms, visually distinguished from the other worms by the absence of true segmentation and their body shape. The phylum includes the parasitic flukes (class Trematoda) and tapeworms (class Cestoda) but its only free-living representatives are Turbellarians.

Class Turbellaria (Free-living flatworms)

Morphology: The terrestrial species are less flattened than their aquatic counterparts, but have a flattened sole. They lack clear segmentation and are bilaterally symmetrical (equally proportioned on either side of the lengthwise mid-line). Eyes are either numerous and scattered around the front (head) end, or a pair of larger eyes. The largest British species can reach 90 mm in length, but the most common rarely reach 25 mm. At least four species are found regularly in damp woods, etc.

Ecology: Predominantly an aquatic group but seven species have been recorded in damp terrestrial habitats – in shady moist woods, under logs, in decaying vegetation and leaf litter, or in damp moss. Very little is known of their biology. The most common species (*Microplana terrestris*) is most likely to be found on moist nights, whereas the remaining species are more strictly subterranean and are only rarely recorded above the ground. The flatworms are carnivorous, feeding on minute molluscs and worms and can be found at most times of the year.

Further details of biology and identification are given in Ball & Reynoldson (1981).

Phylum NEMERTEA (Ribbon worms)

Non-segmented and difficult to distinguish from flatworms (class Turbellaria, see p. 53). The two groups were combined as one by early naturalists, and nemerteans are still sometimes regarded as a class within the phylum Platyhelminthes. One British representative occurs in terrestrial habitats. *Argonemertes dendyi* has an eversible proboscis which will distinguish live specimens from closely similar flatworms (see notes above). Up to 25 mm long. The eyes in this species are arranged in two groups of 3 or 8. This contrasts with the arrangement in flatworms. Two stripes run lengthways along the whole of the body, whereas in flatworms which share a similar pattern the stripes usually merge or become indistinct some way short of the head end.

Ecology: *A. dendyi* lives in damp shady places, usually under stones and wood in dense copses and near streams. Recorded from Ireland, Wales and the south coast of England. It is thought to be a predator on immature and soil-dwelling insects (including springtails, bugs and myriapods), feeding by everting its proboscis and sucking the juices of its prey.

Further details are given in Pantin (1969) and Gibson (1994).

Phylum ANNELIDA

The segmented worms. Terrestrial species are never flattened.

Class Hirudinea (Leeches)

Morphology: Many-segmented worms which have suckers at each end of the body. A common species on land (*Haemopsis sanguisuga*) can reach 50 mm in length.

Ecology: No British leech is truly terrestrial, the only land-dwelling forms being found in damp tropical habitats. However, two British species (*H. sanguisuga* and *Trocheta subviridis*) are amphibious and may be found considerable distances from their aquatic homes, sometimes in gardens, usually under stones or in the soil. The amphibious leeches are carnivorous, feeding on small insects, worms and slugs. They do not suck blood and are harmless to humans. Although some aquatic leeches do leave water they are restricted to banks and soil very close to the water's edge.

Further details of ecology and identification are given in Mann (1962 & 1964) and Elliott & Mann (1979).

Class Oligochaeta (Earthworms and potworms)

Morphology: Soft bodied worms with obvious external segmentation. In adults, some segments are broadened and slightly fused to form a band (the clitellum). Two families are represented in terrestrial habitats: the earthworms (family Lumbricidae) and the potworms (family Enchytraeidae). Potworms are usually pale in colour and rarely reach 25 mm, whereas the earthworms may be heavily pigmented and can reach 250 mm.

Ecology: Most of the terrestrial worms live exclusively in the soil, but can be found in dense and moist leaf litter or decaying vegetation. All worms avoid the surface during daylight hours, but some species emerge from the ground at night when optimum temperatures and humidity occur. The lob worm (*Lumbricus terrestris*) is unusual in that it also mates on the surface.

Vertical stratification within the soil may occur, with different species of earthworm in zones of increasing depth. Potworms are unable to burrow, so are largely restricted in movement to fissures and crevices, or burrows made by other animals. Populations as large as 850 individuals per surface square metre of soil have been recorded. They feed on organic detritus (dead leaves, twigs, etc.). Life cycles, and frequency of occurrence at different times of the year, varies between species.

Edwards & Lofty (1972) and Sims & Gerard (1999) give further information on biology and identification of earthworms. O'Connor (1967) provides a detailed introduction to the enchytraeids. An AIDGAP key to earthworms is available (Sherlock, 2012).

Phylum ARTHROPODA

This phylum contains over 80% of the animals described so far, world-wide – more than 1.25 million species. The main distinguishing features are the hardened external skeleton with three or more pairs of tubular, jointed legs. Cloudsley-Thompson & Sankey (1961) give a general introduction to the biology and taxonomy of non-insect groups, whilst Chinery (2012) does the same for the insect orders.

Subphylum Chelicerata

The name of this group is derived from the specialised front appendages which form claws, or chelae, although these are not always obvious. Only one class, the Arachnida, has successfully invaded the land and is represented by five orders in Britain. Jones (1984) serves as a useful introduction to the group as a whole, and Cloudsley-Thompson & Sankey (1961) cover all groups with the exception of the scorpions.

Class Arachnida

Mainly predators with over 50,000 species worldwide. Four pairs of legs; no antennae; no wings. See Cloudsley-Thompson & Sankey (1961) and Jones (1984).

Order Scorpiones (Scorpions)

Morphology: The head and thorax are fused and are covered by a single shield (the carapace). The front appendages are modified into powerful chelicerae and a pair of large claws. The abdomen is extended into a narrowing tail ending in a sting. Four pairs of walking legs. The poison gland is located in the sting, but the British representative (*Euscorpius flavicaudis*) is generally harmless to humans and rarely exceeds 40 mm. Live young are carried on the abdomen of their mother until they have moulted, after which they disperse. Immatures are easily recognisable as scorpions.

Ecology: Unlike other arachnids, the scorpions lack silk glands and are unable to spin webs or weave egg sacs or refuges. They have poor sight and are primarily nocturnal, spending the day resting in crevices in walls or under stone. *Euscorpius flavicaudis* has been found at Sheerness in Kent for over 100 years, and has also been recorded in other port towns on the south coast of England. See Wanless (1977) for further details.

Order Pseudoscorpiones (False scorpions)

Morphology: With large claws, but lack the abdominal tail and sting which are characteristic of the true scorpions. Poison glands are contained in the claws. The largest British species reach only 4 mm. Young are carried on the mother's abdomen and disperse only after moulting. They cannot be confused with any other group.

Ecology: Active predators, feeding on minute animals such as psocids (see p. 69) and collembola (see p. 62). Most occur in moss, leaf litter, the top layer of soil or under stones and loose bark. Two of the 26 British species are found in houses, where they feed on other arthropods including house mites and bed bugs. Pseudoscorpions have been found clinging to other insects, but this is not a parasitic relationship – the 'hosts' are being used simply for transport, a practice known as phoresy.

The synopsis by Legg & Jones (1988) is the most comprehensive recent guide. Further information is available at Gerald Legg's website (www.chelifer.com).

Order Araneae (Spiders)

Morphology: Distinguished from other arachnids by the presence of a narrow waist, known as the pedicel. The hind end lacks the obvious segmentation characteristic of all other arachnid groups with the exception of the mites and ticks (see Acari below). Following hatching, the young undergo a series of moults becoming increasingly like their parents. However, even the most immature spiders are unlikely to be confused with any other group.

Ecology: An enormously diverse group, with over 650 species in Britain. Mainly predators on other arthropods, predominantly insects. Spiders have the ability to spin silk but this is used to a varying extent. Some spin webs to catch prey, others only use the silk to manufacture refuges or protective sacs for their eggs. The silk may also be used as a means of transport. Smaller spiders spin fine threads which are caught in air-currents carrying the spiders to considerable heights and for large distances. This practice, known as ballooning, ensures that spiders are often the first animals to colonise a new site and can be found in habitats throughout the whole of Britain.

Bristowe (1958) provides a useful introduction to natural history of the British fauna; the keys in three volumes by Locket & Millidge (1951 & 1953) and Locket, Millidge & Merrett (1974) cover most but not all British species. An AIDGAP key to families of British spiders is available (Jones-Walters, 1989). Roberts (1995) is a useful introductory guide, but is less comprehensive for the money spiders. An FSC fold-out chart to house and garden spiders has been produced (Bee & Lewington, 2002).

Order Opiliones (Harvestmen)

Morphology: Harvestmen lack the waist of the spiders and are usually also distinguished by the presence of visible segmentation on the lower abdomen (although this may be indistinct in some species). They usually have a wart-like tubercle (the ocularium) on the upper side of the carapace, on which the eyes are situated. In most species, the walking legs are very long, extending to several times the body length, but they are much shorter in some groups inhabiting leaf litter. The young start moulting almost immediately after hatching and this is repeated 7-8 times before reaching maturity. Even at the youngest stages most nymphs are recognisable as harvestmen.

Ecology: All of the British harvestmen are predominantly carnivorous, feeding on a variety of invertebrates, usually through active nocturnal predation but also whilst scavenging. They do not use webs for trapping. 28 (possibly 29) species occur in Britain. The group is widespread, occurring throughout Britain and in most terrestrial habitats. Representatives can be found at any time of the year.

Biology and identification are covered by Sankey & Savory (1974). A synopsis (Hillyard, 2005) and an FSC fold-out chart to harvestmen have been produced (Richards, 2010).

Subclass Acari (Mites and ticks)

Morphology: Almost all free-living Acari are smaller than 2 mm, displaying an enormous variation in external appearance. They can be distinguished from spiders by the absence of a waist, and from harvestmen by the absence of both the external segmentation and the ocularium. Most species of mites and ticks possess an obvious head region, the capitulum. The life-history stages are still uncertain for most species, but the majority of Acari hatch as six-legged larvae which are usually followed by one or more eight-legged nymphal stages, before becoming sexually-mature adults. Some mites live exclusively in plant galls – these may have only two pairs of legs. The number of larval and nymphal instars (stages between moults), and the external form that they take may vary as a result of habitat condition at that time. Similarly, the developmental stages can be either parasitic or free living.

Ecology: Over 1500 species of mites and ticks have been recorded in Britain and many more remain to be found. A great variety of lifestyles have been developed; even within the same species the life history stages may have a contrasting ecology. The ticks are ectoparasitic Acari which feed on vertebrate blood but spend most of the time in vegetation, attaching themselves to their hosts only when feeding. Likewise, most other groups have representatives which are parasitic at some stage in their life-cycle. This parasitism may have developed through the phoretic behaviour of many mites, whereby they hitch lifts on the bodies of other animals (see also the notes on pseudoscorpions). Whilst a large number of Acari are carnivorous, mainly feeding through parasitism and scavenging rather than active predation, some species are predominantly plant feeders often through sucking the sap of their hosts. Spider mites may cause considerable damage to horticultural crops in this way, while some mites spread virus diseases and cause galls. The oribatid mites are usually the most abundant group of arthropods in litter and soil, feeding on decaying organic matter and associated fungi and bacteria. Acari are widespread, forming an important part of the invertebrate fauna in most habitats – one estimate was for 500 million mites per acre in some British grasslands.

Cloudsley-Thompson & Sankey (1961) provide an introduction to the group, but Evans et al. (1961) give a fully-comprehensive coverage, whilst Arthur (1963) deals with the ticks alone. A synopsis (Hillyard, 1996) has been produced.

Subphylum Crustacea

Crustaceans have two pairs of antennae, although one pair is very inconspicuous in woodlice. The body is protected by a hard exoskeleton.

Class Malacostraca

This is the largest of the six classes of Crustacea. Although predominantly aquatic animals, two groups within this class (the orders Isopoda and Amphipoda) are represented in British terrestrial habitats.

Order Isopoda (Woodlice)

Morphology: Woodlice are only likely to be confused with one other group, the pill millipedes (see p. 60) but can be distinguished from the latter by their having a number of narrow segments at the hind end with projecting appendages (the uropods). The uropods are difficult to see in the pillbug woodlice, *Armadillidium* spp. They are flattened, with seven pairs of walking legs as adults. However, very young larvae (which hatch in a late stage of development) may have the last pair of legs incomplete. Woodlice have rudimentary abdominal gills, a legacy from the aquatic existence which is characteristic of the crustacea as a whole. The gills, although being protected by plates which hide them from view, are still prone to water loss and this restricts most of these animals to humid habitats and a nocturnal lifestyle. An increasing specialisation to terrestrial life can be seen across the various representatives, the better adapted groups being more able to remain active during daylight hours.

Ecology: 40 species of woodlice have been recorded as native or naturalised in Britain, plus a further 12 alien species restricted to glasshouses. All are scavengers, feeding on dead or dying plant material, and their own droppings (thus increasing the efficiency of the digestive process). Most are nocturnal and found in humid habitats. The eggs are carried by the mother until they hatch. The young resemble the adults but may lack a pair of legs; these early stages are often found in broods which are attended by the mother until later stages of development. Woodlice can be found at any time of the year.

A synopsis (Oliver & Meechan, 1993), AIDGAP guide (Hopkin, 1991) and FSC fold-out chart (Hopkin, 2003) are available. Gregory (2009) includes useful information about collecting and recording. See also the British Myriapod and Isopod Group's website (www.bmig.org.uk).

Order Amphipoda (Sandhoppers and scuds)

Morphology: Up to 15 mm long. Shrimp-like: compressed side-to-side and curled up (usually). Eleven pairs of 'legs', but these are specialised into walking, swimming and jumping appendages. Two pairs of antennae. The relative length of the antennae will help to separate these from the aquatic amphipods. The upper pair are clearly shorter than the lower pair, their whole length being shorter than the peduncle (the enlarged basal segments) of the lower antennae. The lower antennae are approximately half as long as the rest of the body.

Ecology: Only one truly terrestrial British species, *Arcitalitrus (Talitroides) dorrieni*. (Other members of the same family – the Talitridae – are semi-terrestrial. Although never fully submerged, they are restricted to the supra-littoral zone on or near the seashore; sand dunes, salt marshes, etc.). *A. dorrieni* is usually found in damp or decaying vegetation, or humus. These animals are probably scavengers but may feed on carrion also. Recorded from the Isles of Scilly originally, but now found in many inland habitats throughout southwest Britain and in isolated localities as far apart as Surrey, Argyll and Co. Galway (Ireland).

Identification and further details are given in Lincoln (1979).

Class Maxilopoda

This class is mainly aquatic, but some members of order Copepoda are found on land.

Order Copepoda

Morphology: Less than 1 mm. Two pairs of antennae; the upper one longer than the lower. The larvae, known as nauplii, are free living and have three pairs of appendages on hatching. Further pairs of legs are added during a series of moults.

Ecology: Little is known, but the terrestrial copepods are likely to feed on decomposing organic matter. They can secrete a slime coating to form a cyst and survive long periods of frost and drought. May be abundant in moist beech litter in Southern England.

Further information is given by Gurney (1931) and by Harding & Smith (1960).

Subphylum Myriapoda

Myriapods have a single pair of antennae.

Class Pauropoda

Morphology: Very small, 0.5 to 2 mm; blind; with uniquely branched antennae; body adorned with pairs of long bristles; ten pairs of legs when adult, but the tiny nymphs (less than 0.2 mm long) hatch with three pairs of legs and only attain the full complement after a series of moults.

Ecology: Very common in soil, but frequently overlooked because of their size. They are thought to feed on dead plant material. Life cycle and population biology are largely unknown, but they can be found throughout Britain at any time of the year.

Class Diplopoda (Millipedes)

Morphology: With few exceptions, the millipedes have long bodies (up to 50 mm), several times longer than broad. Some are almost circular in cross section and this will help to distinguish them from the more flattened centipedes. They also lack the anterior poison claws (the forcipules), and have two pairs of legs per body segment compared to a single pair in centipedes. They will also have less than 10 antennal segments, whereas centipedes have more. Some groups have over 80 pairs of legs. Unfortunately, the adults of some groups do not conform to the general description. Pill millipedes (*Glomerida*) may be confused with woodlice, but lack the complex segmentation at the rear of the abdomen. The bristly *Polyxenus lagurus* (Polyxenida) is easily mistaken for a larva of the beetle *Ctesias serras*, but does have millipede characters when examined closely. Others have keels on the side of each segment, giving a flat-backed appearance (Polydesmida: Chordeumatida (suborder Craspedosomatidea)), and are often confused with centipedes but can be separated by the double-pairs of legs, the absence of a pair of poison claws (forcipules) and the antennal segmentation.

The larvae hatch with three (or four) pairs of legs and gain their full complement after a number of moults. The early stage could be confused with minute soil-dwelling insects, particularly springtails. Millipede larvae will rarely have only six abdominal segments, will not have antennae originating from the upper side of the face, nor will they have any ventral tubes or springing organs; springtails will have one or more of these characters.

Ecology: 58 native and naturalised British species, plus at least 6 alien species found in glasshouses. Mainly soil or leaf litter dwellers, but will use other habitats opportunistically. For example, cowpats and manure will often provide temporary homes for large numbers of millipedes. All are detritivores, feeding on dead plant material, but some species will feed on fungi and dead animals, whilst others will crop fresh vegetation. In drought, the latter may infest arable crops and can become pests.

Hopkin & Read (1992) is the most up-to-date and comprehensive account of the biology of millipedes. Lee (2006) gives the most recent account of the ecology. Wheater & Read (1996) contains some useful introductory keys. A Synopsis has been produced (Blower, 1985) but it is out of print and is difficult to obtain. See also the British Myriapod and Isopod Group's website (www.bmig.org.uk).

Class Chilopoda (Centipedes)

Morphology: Very variable in size (up to 80 mm), and morphology. The flattened body form, and presence of poison claws (the forcipules) at the head end, will distinguish the centipedes from millipedes. Also, the latter have two pairs of legs per body segment whereas centipedes have one pair only. Centipedes have more than 14 antennal segments, often many more. The number of legs in adults varies between the four orders, from a minimum of 15 pairs to over one hundred.

Immature geophilomorph centipedes hatch with a full complement of legs, but in the other two orders the larvae have a reduced number, four or five pairs, and additional pairs are added as the animals undergo a series of moults before maturation.

Ecology: 47 native and naturalised British species. There are also 3 species of dubious status, and approximately 10 more species of glasshouse aliens. The centipedes are prone to water loss and the majority are nocturnal predators, favouring humid habitats. They may take refuge deep underground, or in crevices during droughts and hard winters; otherwise, they can be found at all times of the year. Prey are actively caught, being immobilised with the aid of a poison gland situated at the base of the claws (British species are harmless to humans, although the largest have been known to pierce skin, creating a sensation which has been described as similar to a wasp sting). The behaviour of each of the three orders is quite distinctive, as is their morphology. The burrowing centipedes (Geophilomorpha) are blind and have long flexible bodies, with relatively short legs, whereas the surface hunters (Lithobiomorpha, Scolopendromorpha and Scutigeromorpha) are able to see, and have stouter and less flexible bodies with longer legs which enable these animals to travel at speed along the ground, using visual cues to seek out their prey, usually surface-dwelling insects.

A full review of the British centipedes' biology, and keys to identification of species, are given in Eason (1964). Lewis (2007) provides a review of the biology of the group. A synopsis (Barber, 2009) and an AIDGAP identification guide (Barber, 2008) are available. See also the British Myriapod and Isopod Group's website (www.bmig.org.uk).

Class Symphyla

Morphology: Can reach 10 mm in length, but usually smaller than 4 mm. Long, thread-like antennae composed of many segments. White. Similar to centipedes, but adults have a maximum of 12 pairs of legs and lack the claws. Juveniles hatch without the full complement of legs, usually six pairs, and add further pairs during the three months taken to reach maturity.

Ecology: Common in upper layers of the soil, feeding mainly on dead plant material. They feed on living roots and in artificial situations, such as greenhouses, they may become pests.

There is relatively little published information about this group. Edwards (1959) and Hopkin & Roberts (1988) are useful. A checklist of British species can be found at the British Myriapod and Isopod Group's website (www.bmig.org.uk).

Subphylum Hexapoda

This sub-phylum includes the insects and also groups which are no longer considered as insects but are classified in class Entognatha: the orders Collembola, Diplura and Protura.

Two texts are particularly recommended: Barnard (2011) gives a comprehensive overview of the taxonomy of all Hexapoda orders, whilst Chinery (2012) is extremely useful for identification, and includes a large number of excellent colour plates.

Class Entognatha

Small wingless arthropods, formerly considered to be primitive orders of insects. The mouthparts are enclosed in a pouch on the head.

Order Collembola (Springtails)

Morphology: Small, up to 5 mm but usually smaller. External appearance varies, but always with a distinctive six-segmented abdomen. The surface dwellers are larger, with longer antennae and legs, often with a forked springing organ and wart-like tube underneath the abdomen. The soil inhabitants have very short legs and antennae and lack the springing organ and tube, and many are tiny (smaller than 1 mm), pale and blind. The nymphs resemble the adults, but are smaller.

Ecology: Approximately 250 British species. Springtails live in soil, leaf litter, grass swards, etc., feeding on dead or dying plant material. They are extremely abundant; one scientist estimated 230 million individuals per acre of meadowland. Adults and nymphs can be found at any time of the year.

Two AIDGAP identification guides are available: a very comprehensive set of keys to species level (Hopkin, 2007) and a concise guide to families (Dallimore & Shaw, 2013).

Order Diplura (Two-pronged bristletails)

Morphology: Small, 3-5 mm; usually white; two tails; thorax clearly divided into three segments; no compound eyes. The nymphs resemble the adults.

Ecology: Eleven British species all belonging to one genus *Campodea*. Widely distributed, in leaf litter and soil, under stones and in any habitat where plant debris is common. They are thought to prey on springtails (Collembola), dead animals and roots. Little is known of their life-history; they breed in the summer but are found throughout the year. Delaney (1954) gives further details of biology and identification.

Order Protura

Morphology: Tiny, less than 2 mm long; pointed head; blind; antennae, if present, very short; pale; 12 abdominal segments in adults, but only nine in recently hatched nymphs. Others are added later, a developmental feature which is unique to proturans, but is common in the Pauropoda, Diplopoda, Chilopoda and Symphyla (see p. 60-61).

Ecology: 15 British species. All are soil dwellers, where they may be abundant, but are also common in leaf litter. Widespread. They are thought to be scavengers, feeding on dead or dying plant and animal material. Their biology is not well known but although some species are at their most active during the summer, others will be found throughout the year. Further information is given by Nosek (1973).

Class Insecta

A huge group, with over one million species worldwide. The recorded number of British species rises almost daily, but already exceeds 20,000. Insects have successfully invaded all terrestrial habitats. Adults usually have three pairs of legs, with three major body divisions – the head, thorax and abdomen. Antennae are usually present.

Insects can be divided into two groups: the Apterygota, which lack wings, and the Pterygota, which have one or two pairs of wings (although some species may be secondarily wingless – they are descended from insects which possessed wings). These two groups are no longer considered to be subclasses.

Apterygota

Order Archeaognatha (Three-pronged bristletails)

Morphology: Cone-shaped body; three long tails; thread-like antennae. They use their tails to spring up into the air. Body (except parts of the head) covered in scales.

Ecology: They live in a wide range of habitats, including buildings, heathlands and rocky shores (sea cliffs), and feed mainly on dying vegetation and detritus.

This order was formerly combined with the Zygentoma to form the order Thysanura. Delaney (1954) gives further details of biology and identification.

Order Zygentoma (Silverfish and firebrats)

Morphology: Cone-shaped body; three long tails; thread-like antennae. Body covered in scales, and may appear silvery. Movement is often sinuous – hence the popular name, 'silverfish'. The immature nymphs resemble the adults. The largest reach 20 mm in length, but most are smaller.

Ecology: The house-dwellers (including the firebrat) favour starchy foods. Although the 'wild-living' forms do seem to have seasonal life-cycles, with eggs being laid in late summer and autumn then hatching in the following spring or early summer, the domestic species can lay and hatch at any time of the year.

This order was formerly combined with the Archeaognatha to form the order Thysanura. Delaney (1954) gives further details of biology and identification.

Pterygota

Orders of insects in the Pterygota can be divided into several groups:

a. Palaeoptera: orders Ephemeroptera (mayflies) and Odonata (dragonflies and damselflies)

b. Polyneoptera: orders Dermaptera (earwigs), Dictyoptera (cockroaches and termites), Orthoptera (grasshoppers and crickets), Phasmida (stick insects) and Plecoptera (stoneflies)

c. Paraneoptera: orders Hemiptera (true bugs), Phthirapera (true lice), Psocoptera (book and bark lice) and Thysanoptera (thrips)

d. Endopterygota: orders Coleoptera (beetles), Diptera (true flies), Hymenoptera (sawflies, bees, ants and wasps), Lepidoptera (butterflies and moths), Mecoptera (scorpionflies), Megaloptera (alderflies), Neuroptera (lacewings), Raphidioptera (snakeflies), Siphonaptera (fleas), Strepsiptera (stylops) and Trichoptera (caddisflies)

Order Ephemeroptera (Mayflies)

Morphology: Adults usually have two or three long tails. Although most have two pairs of wings, the hind pair is much smaller and is missing in some species. The antennae are short, being scarcely longer than the width of the head at most. The subimago – a developmental stage between nymph and adult which is unique to the mayflies – resembles the adult but has dull and opaque wings which are fringed with short hairs. Also, the tail bristles and legs may be shorter than in the adult stage.

Ecology: 51 British species. Widely distributed. Eggs are laid in water, and the nymphs are entirely aquatic. The earliest species begin to emerge from water around May – hence the name.

The length of time spent in the subimaginal stage varies between species, from several hours to many weeks, and is extended in colder conditions. The adult stages often last only two or three days, during which they may not feed. Both can fly, but the subimago is often found sheltering in vegetation near the water's edge. Male mayflies may swarm at certain times of year, particularly during summer evenings.

Macan (1969) and Elliot & Humpesch (1983) give full details of biology and identification. An AIDGAP guide is available (Macadam & Bennett, 2010).

Order Odonata (Dragonflies and damselflies)

Morphology: Often large (up to 80 mm in overall length). Head is wide, with large globular eyes. Antennae are short, never longer than half the width of the head. The two pairs of wings are fully membranous, and may be pigmented. The order is divided into two suborders: suborder Zygoptera (damselflies) and suborder Anisoptera (dragonflies). Damselflies have both wings similar in size and shape, folded back over the abdomen when at rest, with eyes which are clearly separated when viewed from above the head. Dragonflies have broader hind wings, and both pairs are held out sideways when at rest. The eyes actually meet, or nearly do so, on top of the head.

Ecology: 57 British species. Although they can be found in a wide range of habitats, they are often restricted to the vicinity of freshwater or wetlands in which they breed. The nymphal stage is entirely aquatic and may last several years but the adult is short-lived, only surviving for one week on average, although many live to three weeks and some as long as eight weeks. The adults are encountered most often on hot sunny days between June and September, and are least numerous in cold wet summers. All are carnivorous, actively preying on flying insects.

Corbet et al. (1960), Keen (1977), Hammond (1985), Aguilar et al. (1986), Gibbons (1986) and McGeery (1986) cover the identification and natural history of the group. Smallshire & Swash (2014) is a photographic guide to 56 species plus vagrants. Cham (2012) is a field guide to the larvae and exuviae. An FSC fold-out chart is available (Brooks & Askew, 1999).

Order Dermaptera (Earwigs)

Morphology: Up to 25 mm long, but usually less than 17 mm; long thread-like antennae, with 50+ segments; shortened wing cases which cover a second pair of membranous wings; two curved pincers, though these are only slightly curved in nymphs and some adult females. Nymphs resemble adults, but lack the wing cases (and a strong curve in their 'pincers'). The youngest, and smallest, nymphs are attended by their mother.

Ecology: Seven British species. Widespread, but prefer to rest in dark crevices during the daylight – hence their English name. Most can fly and may be taken in light traps at night. Smaller species measure less than 5 mm when fully grown and are easily overlooked. Feed primarily on plant material, but may be omnivorous, sometimes preying on small arthropods. Earwigs are less likely to be found in winter months during which adults hibernate: in subterranean retreats; on fence posts; under bark, etc. Nymphs are mainly encountered during spring but will be found at any time of the year.

Hincks (1956), Marshall & Haes (1990) and Brindle (1977) give further information, and identification to species. The FSC fold-out chart British grasshoppers and allied insects includes earwigs (Marshall & Ovenden, 1999).

Order Dictyoptera (Cockroaches and termites)

Morphology: Sometimes large (up to 35 mm), flattened insects, with a large pronotum which projects forwards covering most of the head. Antennae are long and thread-like, usually as long as the body. Biting mouthparts; never with piercing mouthparts. May be winged or wingless. The hind end of the abdomen terminates with two stout 'tails'. Although the earliest immatures are worm-like, they moult almost immediately after hatching and the subsequent nymphal stages resemble the adults.

Ecology: Although 11 species are found in Britain, most are restricted to heated buildings and outhouses. Only three are truly 'native', outdoor-living, species and these are most likely to be encountered in Southern England. All are nocturnal omnivorous scavengers. They move rapidly when disturbed. Domestic species can be found at all times of the year, at any stage in the life cycle. They overwinter as eggs, or late-stage nymphs, and reach maturity in May and June, mating soon thereafter, and dying towards the end of the year.

Ragge (1965) and Marshall & Haes (1990) provide detailed information on biology and identification of the British species. The FSC fold-out chart British grasshoppers and allied insects includes cockroaches (Marshall & Ovenden, 1999).

Order Orthoptera (Grasshoppers and crickets)

Morphology: A diverse group, both in size (body length up to 50 mm) and body form. However, all have well-developed back legs which are clearly suited for jumping, and the majority have a well developed saddle-shaped pronotum. They may be winged, with the first of the two pairs sometimes being thick and 'leathery' in the basal part. Many have rudimentary wings, whilst others are completely wingless. Metamorphosis is incomplete; nymphs, although 'worm-like' for a short time after hatching, moult quickly and resemble the mature forms.

The order is divided into five superfamilies:

a. Acroidea: grasshoppers. 11 species. They have short and thick antennae, which are no more than half as long as the body

b. Tetrigoidea: groundhoppers, 3 species. They have short and thick antennae like the grasshoppers, but can be distinguished easily by the form of the pronotum. This is very large in groundhoppers and extends backwards to cover most of the abdomen.

c. Grylloidea: crickets. 5 species. They have long thread-like antennae and large ovipositors. The tarsi are three-segmented. This group includes the mole crickets, which have short antennae that are a third as long as the body at most, and greatly enlarged forelegs.

d. Rhaphidophoroidea: camel crickets. 1 species. They are wingless, with long antennae, and two exeptionally long abdominal 'tails', as well as the ovipositor in females. These are as long as the pronotum, which is never true for other families.

e. Tettigonioidea: bush crickets. 13 species. They have long thread-like antennae, always considerably longer than the body length, with the legs terminating in four-segmented tarsi. Females have a large, curved ovipositor.

Ecology: Camel crickets and mole crickets are very rare. The former is restricted to greenhouses, the latter to a few sites in Southern England (and the Channel Islands). The grasshoppers are widely distributed, as are groundhoppers, but bush crickets are mainly restricted to the southern half of England. Adults of all groups are most common in the summer, but whereas grasshoppers and bush crickets overwinter (November-May) as eggs, ground hoppers and crickets may 'hibernate' as late-stage nymphs. The diet of grasshoppers and ground-hoppers is exclusively vegetarian, the former feeding primarily on grasses, the latter on algae and mosses. Although most bush crickets are also herbivorous, some are known to be carnivorous. Activity rhythms also differ. Grasshoppers and groundhoppers are most active during the day, whereas bush crickets are particularly active at night. Grasshoppers, crickets and bush crickets have characteristic 'songs', produced by rubbing legs and/or wings together, and these can be used to identify the groups. These songs have been recorded and are available on the record which accompanied Ragge's (1965) book which remains the most comprehensive introduction to the biology and identification of the Orthoptera (but also includes Phasmida and Dictyoptera, see opposite and above); unfortunately, both are now very difficult to obtain. A full revision, with an accompanying cassette, is available (Marshall & Haes, 1990). Brown (1983) provides a useful *Synopsis* for the grasshoppers and bush crickets. The FSC fold-out chart *British grasshoppers and allied insects* includes the Orthoptera (Marshall & Ovenden, 1999).

Order Phasmida (Stick insects)

Morphology: Unmistakeable. Often large (up to 90 mm), slender insects. Nymphs resemble adults.

Ecology: There are no native British species but, because of their popularity as laboratory insects and pets, escapees may be found in gardens or school grounds. Some colonies survive in greenhouses. Outdoor colonies are restricted to Devon, Cornwall and the Isles of Scilly. Vegetarian. Nocturnal.

Information on biology and identification is given in Ragge (1965), Marshall & Haes (1990) and Chinery (2012). Also known as the Phasmotodea.

Order Plecoptera (Stoneflies)

Morphology: Usually have two pairs of wings, with the hind pair being larger, but in some males these can be reduced in size. The wings are usually tightly folded over their flattened body, but in some species may be laid flat. Two tails are present in some, but not all, species. The antennae are long; as long as the body in many species.

Ecology: Thirty-four British species. Widespread, but most common near stony streams. The nymphs are aquatic but most are restricted to oxygen-rich waters and as such are useful indicators of contamination. Stoneflies can fly, particularly on sunny days, but often prefer to run when disturbed. The adults, which may only live for two or three weeks, are thought to feed on lichens and algae (if at all).

Hynes (1977) gives full details of biology and identification, and practical information is given by Macan (1982). An AIDGAP guide is available (Pryce et al., 2007).

Order Hemiptera (Bugs)

Morphology: A large group including a wide range of forms. Most can be distinguished from other insect groups by their sucking mouthparts, but these are reduced, or missing altogether (e.g. male scale insects), from some Hemiptera.

This order is separated into four suborders:

a. Heteroptera: approximately 560 species, although some of these live in freshwater rather than terrestrial habitats. A key character is that the base of the forewings is thickened. They include shieldbugs, lace-bugs, damsel bugs and capsid bugs. Many are herbivores, including some horticultural pests, while a few are predators, and some (such as bed bugs) feed on blood.
b. Cicadomorpha: approximately 380 species. Their forewings are entirely uniform, often hardened or leathery throughout. Many species have enlarged back legs for jumping. They include froghoppers, leafhoppers and treehoppers. All are terrestrial herbivores, feeding on plant sap.
c. Fulguromorpha: approximately 85 species. Their forewings are entirely uniform. They include planthoppers. All are terrestrial herbivores, with some feeding on plant roots in the soil.

d.   Sternorrhyncha: approximately 880 species. Their forewings are entirely uniform, and
     are generally soft and membranous. They include aphids, scale insects and mealy bugs.
     Some groups are secondarily wingless, with wings missing or reduced to short wing
     pads. The scale insects and mealy bugs are the most likely to cause confusion. The
     females, sometimes legless as well as wingless, may appear grub-like, whilst males have
     one pair of wings and no sucking mouthparts. All are terrestrial herbivores, feeding on
     plant sap, and include some horticultural pests.

Traditionally the last three suborders were combined into the now-obsolete suborder
Homoptera.

The most comprehensive text for Heteroptera is by Southwood & Leston (1959), whilst
keys in Volume 2 of the Royal Entomological Society's *Handbooks to the Identification of
British Insects* series enables identification to species level in some groups of homoptera.
An up-to-date RES Handbook to Aphids has been published (Blackman, 2010). An AIDGAP
guide for identification of Hemiptera to family level is available (Unwin, 2001). There is also
a photographic guide to shieldbugs and squashbugs (Evans & Edmonson, 2005) and an FSC
fold-out chart to the shieldbugs and allied insects (New, 2004). The British Bugs website
(www.britishbugs.org.uk) is very useful.

Order Phthiraptera (True lice)

This order is divided into four suborders, three of which are found in Britain:

a.   Amblycera: biting lice. Approximately 170 species. Adults are less than 6 mm long,
     rarely more than 3 mm. Body is flattened side-to-side. Antennae inconspicuous, eyes
     reduced or absent, wings missing. Biting mouthparts. The head is as wide as, or wider
     than, the broadest part of the thorax. Nymphs are similar, but smaller, and also spend
     their lives on the host.

b.   Anoplura: sucking lice. Approximately 25 species. They are rarely larger than 3 mm.
     Antennae short, eyes inconspicuous, wings absent. The mouthparts are adapted for
     sucking rather than biting. Nymphs resemble adults. They are all external parasites on
     mammals, including humans.

c.   Ischnocera. Approximately 350 species. They are mostly parasites on birds, but some
     species live on livestock such as cattle and sheep, and can be pests.

Traditionally the suborders Amblycera, Ischnocera and Rhyncophthirina (no British
representatives) were combined in the now-obsolete suborder Mallophaga.

Species are restricted by their hosts' distribution, rather than geographical factors, and
many are found worldwide. They may be found at any time of the year. Further information
and identification is given by Clay (1969 & 1970). Keys are applicable worldwide, e.g. Ferris
(1961).

Order Psocoptera (Booklice and barklice)

Morphology: Small, up to 6 mm. Booklice can be winged (alate) or wingless (apterous). Antennae are long and thread-like. In wingless forms the nymphs resemble adults and can only be distinguished by two-segmented tarsi compared to the three segments found after maturation (although some adults also have only two tarsal segments). In winged forms the nymphs have fleshy wing pads which lack venation whereas the adults' wings are fully membranous and veined. Psocids may be confused with some bugs (Hemiptera), and small sawflies and wasps (Hymenoptera). Bugs will have piercing mouth-parts whereas psocids' are of the biting type. The wing venation and number of tarsal segments will distinguish the psocids from the Hymenoptera.

Ecology: Appriximately 100 British species. Many are tree-dwellers, but some live indoors. Microflora – small fungi, pollen grains, etc. – are the main food source, but house-dwellers feed on moulds growing on old books, thus giving this group their name. Nymphs resemble adults, but lack fully developed wings and/or tarsal segments (see above). Psocids can be found at all times of the year.

New (2006) gives more details of the group's biology and takes identification to species level.

Order Thysanoptera (Thrips)

Morphology: Small, usually less than 3 mm long. Moderately long antennae, often as long as the width of the head. Piercing mouthparts – but these are not obvious. Long and slender body, with habit of curving abdomen upwards when disturbed. Wings (if present) appear as narrow straps fringed with long hairs. Nymphs or, very rarely, active pupae, may have hairless wing pads and may be confused with Psocoptera (booklice), but the shorter antennae and the lack of a 'neck' will distinguish the thrips. Apart from the lack of fully developed wings, and having fewer antennal and tarsal segments, nymphs resemble adults except in colour. Nymphs are generally creamy white or yellow, while adults are invariably darker, usually brownish black.

Ecology: Approximately 180 species. Mainly plant sap feeders, but some may be predators. Some are crop pests. Thysanoptera may fly in large numbers in humid conditions; hence their other common name – thunder flies.

Further details are given in Lewis (1973), Mound et al. (1976) and Kirk (1996).

Order Coleoptera (Beetles)

Morphology: A huge order, with approximately 4000 species in Britain. The vast majority have two pairs of wings when mature, with the first pair modified into a hardened wing case (the elytra) which meet down the midline of the upper abdomen. The rove beetles, and some other groups, are characterised by having truncated elytra which only partly cover the abdomen. These may be confused with earwigs (Dermaptera) but never have anal pincers. Another common mistake is to identify bugs (Hemiptera) as beetles, and vice versa. The two groups can be separated by their mouthparts; beetles are always of the biting form, with well developed jaws and segmented palps, whereas those of the bugs are almost always modified into sucking tubes which are held under the body, and lacking segmented palps. Some adult beetles, the female 'glow worm' for example, are completely wingless. These may be mistaken for larvae of other beetles and, occasionally, lacewings (Neuroptera). However, the mouthparts, five-segmented tarsi and full complement of 11 antenna/segments will distinguish the adult beetles. The beetle larvae undergo complete metamorphosis, but can vary between active free-living forms with well-developed legs to others which are maggot-like and lack any appendages. The latter are rarely free-living, usually tunnelling in stems and leaves or in the underground nests of insect hosts on whose larvae they feed.

Ecology: Beetles occupy all terrestrial, and most aquatic, habitats, and utilise all food sources. Many are active predators, whilst others are entirely herbivorous. Scavengers are also well represented. The adults can be found at any time of the year. The larvae display a similar range of habits. Although the more primitive forms are active predators many others are not free-living, spending their existence tunnelling in stems and leaves, or in the soil, feeding on plant material. The larvae of some parasitic species adopt both lifestyles during their development. After eggs are laid by the adults, the first stage larvae are active and search for the nest of a host. Having found a suitable nest, the larvae moult, becoming increasingly maggot-like until they complete their development by metamorphosing into mature adults. This cycle of 'regressive' development is known as hypermetamorphosis.

Identification and reviews of the biology of beetles are given by Linssen (1959), Walsh & Dibb (1974), Crowson (1981) and Harde & Hammond (1984). The AIDGAP key by Unwin (1984) takes identification of adults to family level. An AIDGAP key to seed and leaf beetles is available (Hubble, 2012). The only comprehensive work enabling identification of British beetles to species level is Joy (1932) but this is now outdated. Duff (2012) is the first part of what will eventually be a four-part replacement for Joy (1932). Volumes 4, 5 and 12 of the Royal Entomological Society's Handbooks series contain specific keys for a number of families. These include carabids (Luff, 2007), weevils (Morris 1997, 2002, 2008, 2012), water beetles (Foster & Friday, 2011; Foster, Bilton & Friday, 2014), rove beetles (Lott, 2009; Lott & Anderson, 2011) and Scraptiidae (Levey, 2009). Cooter & Barclay (2006) provide a good introduction to practical work with the Coleoptera. Mark Telfer's website (markgtelfer.co.uk/beetles) provides an excellent resource on beetles, including collecting and preparation techniques as well as updates on the literature and many unpublished keys not readily available elsewhere. FSC fold-out charts to ladybird adults (Majerus et al., 2006) and to the larvae and pupae of ladybirds are available (Brown et al., 2012).

Order Diptera (True flies)

Morphology: A huge group, displaying great structural diversity. Almost all have a single pair of wings, with the second pair modified into balancers (halteres). The presence and location of the halteres, and the form of the mouthparts (always of the sucking type, but sometimes adapted for piercing or cutting) will distinguish the Diptera from other two-winged insects: mayflies (Ephemeroptera); bugs (Hemiptera); Strepsiptera. Some parasitic or phoretic forms have lost both sets of wings. Life histories are sometimes complex, particularly in the parasites, but all larvae undergo complete metamorphosis before maturation and do not resemble the adults. The larvae never have true legs, but may have prolegs. The larvae of the more 'primitive' families have a well developed head capsule whereas this has been lost in the more 'advanced' groups. The latter have enclosed mouthparts which should be visible under strong light, particularly if the specimen is gently squeezed between two slides.

Ecology: It is impossible to summarise the biology of this large group (approximately 7000 British species) in the space available here. The true flies flies occupy all terrestrial habitats as adults, and the larvae are found also in many aquatic habitats. They are found at all times of the year. All food sources are utilised, but the larvae feed primarily on decaying animal and vegetable matter.

The biology of the British Diptera is described in Colyer & Hammond (1968), and further useful information is contained in the *Dipterist's Handbook* (Chandler, 2010). An AIDGAP key to families is available (Unwin, 1981). The hoverflies (family Syrphidae) are a group which have attracted particular interest, with the books by Stubbs & Falk (2002), Ball & Morris (2013) and Gilbert (1986) giving wide-ranging introductions to ecology and identification in this group. For soldierflies, see Stubbs & Drake (2014). Volumes 9 and 10 of the Royal Entomological Society's *Handbooks for the identification of British insects* series deal with individual families of Diptera.

Order Hymenoptera (Sawflies, bees, ants and wasps)

Approximately 7000 British species. An extremely large and varied group of four-winged (occasionally secondarily wingless) insects consisting of two contrasting suborders.

a. Suborder Symphyta

Morphology: Vary greatly in size, up to 40 mm. Four-winged, lacking a constricted waist. The wings may be reduced in some rare cases, but most often have complex venation with at least three closed cells in the forewings. Females may have obvious 'stings' (the ovipositors) which are used for drilling the wood in which eggs are laid-hence their common name, the wood wasps. The larvae may be free-living, whilst others are tunnellers in leaves and stems or develop inside Rosaceae fruits, galls or leaf rolls. The galls and leaf rolls are particularly common on willows (*Salix* spp.). The free-living larvae resemble caterpillars but have more abdominal prolegs, at least six pairs, and may be large, up to 25 mm. The enclosed larvae have lost the prolegs and may be confused with some beetle larvae.

Ecology: Adult sawflies feed mainly on pollen or honeydew, but some are predators. They are found on vegetation in a wide range of habitats, from spring through to late autumn. Most larvae are herbivorous, feeding primarily on one particular foodplant.

b. Suborder Apocrita

Morphology: The Apocrita are traditionally divided into two groups: Parasitica and Aculeata. The Parasitica contains over 5000 parasitic species. The Aculeata contains over 600 species belonging to the non-parasitic solitary and social groups of ants, bees and wasps. Several large families combine both lifestyles. There is considerable variation in morphology and habit. However, all share one common feature – the constricted waist. Most adults have four-wings, but many are wingless. The females of many parasitic species have long sting-like ovipositors whereas the social groups do not. Other differences occur in the wing venation; this can be quite complex in some insects but is almost totally absent in others. Larvae have no legs, are never free-living, and usually lack any well-defined head capsule.

Ecology: The Apocrita display a great range of lifestyles. It includes many parasitic species, the gall-forming wasps, the solitary hunting wasps and bees, and the colony-forming social bees, ants and wasps. With the exception of the gall wasps and bees, the aculeate larvae are always fed on the bodies of invertebrates, often the larvae of other insect groups. In parasitic species the eggs are laid in, or near, the body of the host, but in hunting species the prey is carried to a nest. Some parasitic species attack other parasites – a phenomenon known as hyperparasitism. The adults feed mainly on nectar and honeydew, but some of the parasitic species have been known to feed on the hosts whilst ovipositing.

Many books deal with the biology of this vast group, but none is comprehensive in itself. Richards (1977) includes a key to all families of Hymenoptera, and AIDGAP keys to genera of Symphyta (Wright, 1990) are available. Keys by Yeo & Corbet (1995) (species of solitary wasps) and Willmer (1985) (genera of all aculeates - the bees, ants and wasps) take identification further. Skinner & Allen (2013) deals with ants; Archer (2014) with vespoid wasps, and Prys-Jones & Corbet (2011) with bumblebees. Edwards & Jenner (2009) is a photographic guide to bumblebees. All include full lists of references for these groups. Volumes 6, 7 and 8 of the Royal Entomolgical Society's Handbooks series will take identification to species level. Useful information is given in the *Hymenopterists' Handbook* (Betts *et al.*, 1986). An FSC fold-out chart is also available (Buglife *et al.*, 2007).

Order Lepidoptera (Moths and butterflies)

Morphology: A very large and diverse group. Adults usually have two pairs of membranous wings, often deeply pigmented and covered in scales. The scales are sparsely distributed between hairs in some groups. Antennae are mostly long, and mouthparts adapted for sucking – the proboscis being long, and often curved or tightly rolled under the body. Some adult Lepidoptera, particularly in the families Nymphalidae, Satyridae and Riodinidae, have greatly reduced forelegs and may appear to have only four legs rather than six. Some moths have lost their mouthparts, and females of others may be wingless. Metamorphosis is complete, with larvae (caterpillars) bearing no resemblance to adults. Some live in cases constructed from silk and vegetational debris; these are known as 'bagworms', mainly belonging to the family Psychidae, and easily separated from other case-forming insect larvae by the presence of abdominal prolegs. Caterpillars may have jointed thoracic legs, but the number of abdominal prolegs varies between groups, from 2 to 8 pairs (including the pair on the last abdominal segment). Those without legs are usually leaf-miners.

Ecology: Approximately 2570 British species. Most adults feed on plant material, usually juices, sap or nectar. Larvae have chewing mouthparts, and are often pests; some are leaf miners, stem borers, root feeders or scavengers – the latter occurring in nests, houses or granaries. However, most larvae are active browsers on vegetation. Moths and butterflies usually hibernate as eggs or pupae, although some overwinter as larvae. Adults are found mainly in the summer but some will be found throughout the year. Adults that do hibernate are often found in houses, dark rooms or sheds.

The size of the group, and their general interest to naturalists, has generated a huge literature. However, the books by Ford (1957), Skinner (1984), Majerus (2002) and Newland *et al.* (2010) will give a wide-ranging introduction to the British Lepidoptera. The first volumes in a comprehensive series dealing with all groups have been published (Heath & Emmet, 1976, onwards). Butterflies are well covered; see Lewington (2003) and Bebbington & Lewington (1998). Waring *et al.* (2009) covers over 880 species of macromoth, while Sterling *et al.* (2012) covers the micromoths. The UK Moths website (www.ukmoths.org.uk) and UK Butterflies website (www.ukbutterflies.co.uk) are useful.

Order Mecoptera (Scorpion flies and snow fleas)

Morphology: The head of adults is extended downwards into a characteristic 'beak'. There are two groups – the winged scorpion flies (three species belonging to the genus *Panorpa*) and the wingless snow fleas (one species, *Boreus hyemalis*). The panorpids possess two pairs of similar wings and the males have a sting-like extension to their abdomen. Although this gives the group its name, it is entirely harmless, and is missing from females. The early larval stages which are active have eight pairs of abdominal 'false' legs in addition to their 'true' jointed thoracic legs, but these are thought to degenerate in the later stages which are exclusively earth-dwelling. The adult snow fleas are small (less than 3 mm in length) and wingless, moving by running rapidly, or jumping. Their larvae are never free-living (see below).

Ecology: The winged panorpid scorpion flies (3 species) are found mainly in the spring and summer, often sunning themselves in or around thickets and hedgerows; dense brambles and nettles are particularly favoured. They are scavengers, feeding on plant juices as well as dead insects and other carrion. Eggs are laid in crevices in the soil, and the active first-stage larva makes it way deeper into the earth or litter. The larvae are thought to be scavengers. The snow fleas (1 species) are also active during the daytime, particularly in the late autumn and winter – hence the group's name. They are most common in damp, mossy areas and their larvae spend all of their time in moss, below the surface. The snow fleas, adults and larvae, appear to feed exclusively on moss, the larvae and pupae being found in small cavities under the surface of the vegetation.

An AIDGAP guide to the lacewings and their allies (Neuroptera, Megaloptera, Raphidioptera and Mecoptera) is available (Plant, 1997).

Order Megaloptera (Alderflies)

Morphology: This order shares a number of characters with lacewings. Adults have two pairs of similar wings with complex venation, long antennae, large compound eyes and an absence of any abdominal tails. However, alderflies are distinct from the lacewings in lacking the forked venation on wing margins. Unlike the snakeflies, there is no pterostigma on the forewings. The larvae also possess a characteristic prothorax but are otherwise dissimilar from the adults. Unusually for insects which undergo full metamorphosis, the short-lived pupal stage is also active. The larvae are aquatic.

Ecology: Adult alderflies (3 species), which live for a few days only, are most often found near water, basking in the sunshine in late-spring to early-summer. They may feed on nectar, if at all. The larvae are aquatic predators.

An AIDGAP guide to the lacewings and their allies (Neuroptera, Megaloptera, Raphidioptera and Mecoptera) is available (Plant, 1997).

Order Neuroptera (Lacewings)

Morphology: With one exception (the family Coniopterygidae), adult Neuropterans can be distinguished by their two pairs of similar wings with complex venation, long antennae, large compound eyes and absence of any abdominal tails. Coniopterygidae do not conform to the normal lacewing pattern; briefly, the adults are small insects (less than 8 mm long), are covered in white powdery wax and have dissimilar sized wings with reduced venation. As with lacewings the larvae undergo complete metamorphosis and do not resemble the adults. They differ from the lacewing larvae by having hairy (plumose) antennae and by lacking the strongly projecting jaws; nevertheless, as with lacewing larvae, their jaws are adapted for sucking (adults in both groups have biting mouthparts). The larval palps are often club-shaped. Length is usually less than 2.5 mm. Adult lacewings have two pairs of similar sized wings, with complex wing venation including parallel leading edge veins and forking at the wing margins. Lacewing larvae are similar in general body shape to the Coniopterygidae larvae, but differ in antennae, which are never plumose, and mouthparts, which never have club-shaped palps (see above). They are often larger, reaching 15 mm in length.

Ecology: 69 species. All are predators, both as larvae and as adults, and are known to take a wide range of small invertebrate prey including aphids. Lacewing adults may also feed on nectar and honeydew – the sugary excretion from aphids. Adults are mainly active at dawn and dusk and will be found resting on vegetation during the day, sometimes in groups. Deciduous woods, and vegetation near rivers and streams, are favoured habitats. The life-cycle is not seasonal and overwintering may occur at any stage.

An AIDGAP guide to the lacewings and their allies (Neuroptera, Megaloptera, Raphidioptera and Mecoptera) is available (Plant, 1997).

Order Raphidioptera (Snakeflies)

Morphology: The snakeflies are distinguished from lacewings and alderflies by their elongated prothorax, the presence of a pigmented spot on the forewing (the pterostigma) and the long egg-laying apparatus (ovipositor) in females. The larvae also possess a characteristic prothorax but are otherwise dissimilar from the adults. Unusually for insects which undergo full metamorphosis, the short-lived pupal stage is also active. Snake fly larvae (and pupae) differ from the lacewing larvae in having biting rather than sucking mouthparts and in having short antennae.

Ecology: Adult snakeflies (3 British species) occur in wooded areas throughout Britain, usually in very thick vegetation, and near rivers and streams. They are active daytime predators, feeding on aphids and other small insects during the spring and early summer. The larvae live under bark (in beetle burrows) and feed on beetle larvae.

An AIDGAP guide to the lacewings and their allies (Neuroptera, Megaloptera, Raphidioptera and Mecoptera) is available (Plant, 1997).

Order Siphonaptera (Fleas)

Morphology: The adult fleas are small (less than 7 mm long), wingless external parasites of vertebrates, which are strongly flattened from side to side. The non-parasitic larvae undergo complete metamorphosis. They are worm-like, sometimes reaching 4 mm in length, and may resemble some dipteran larvae (see p. 70). Flea larvae are always restricted to the nests of their prospective hosts.

Ecology: The 62 British species are all blood-sucking external parasites as adults, using a wide range of hosts. However, most species are associated with a particular host. Free-living adults will be taken usually in the vicinity of the dead host (or in its nest), and are more likely to leave the protection of the host's body in warmer weather. Fleas are active throughout the year, often jumping considerable distances when disturbed. The free-living larvae feed on detritus in the hosts' nests.

Further details for biology and identification are given by Whittaker (2007).

Order Strepsiptera (Stylops)

Morphology: The free-living male is less than 3 mm long, has one pair of wings, with the front wings reduced to club-shaped halteres. Distinctive, branched antennae. The wings are very broad, and have reduced venation. The female developes in the host (see below) and is worm-like. Eggs and larvae also develop within hosts, but may have a short-lived free-living stage shortly after hatching.

Ecology: 10 British species. All are parasites, mainly on Hymenoptera but also on Hemiptera. Active free-living Strepsipteran larvae emerge from their adult host and may be taken on flowers, etc. whilst waiting to attach to another adult which will be used to transport them back to a nest where they eventually parasitise the host species' larvae. Although present in large numbers shortly after hatching, the Strepsipteran larvae are only rarely found.

Little information is available for this group but Unwin (1984) takes identification of adults to family level and Linssen (1959) gives more details on life-history.

Order Trichoptera (Caddis flies)

Morphology: Most adults are four-winged and moth-like, but are covered in minute hairs rather than scales. The long antennae, absence of a coiled proboscis, and the type of wing venation will also help to separate the caddis flies from most moths, and other groups with which they could be confused – the mayflies and alder flies in particular. Females of one rare species – *Enoicyla pusilla* – are wingless. Most immature larvae are exclusively aquatic, but *E. pusilla* is terrestrial. These larvae live in a case made of sand grains and fragments of dead plant material, measuring up to 10 mm in length, which is carried around during active periods.

Ecology: 198 British species. Most adults are found near the freshwater habitats in which development to maturity has taken place. Males may swarm, particularly toward dusk. Many are nocturnal fliers. The adults may live for several weeks, but many are short-lived and will not feed. The wingless females of *E. pusilla* will be encountered rarely, but are found between September and November; their terrestrial cased larvae develop through to May/June of the following year. The immatures have been found only in deciduous (e.g. oak, beech, small-leaved lime) leaf litter although they may persist amongst conifers which have been planted to replace broadleaved trees. Rarely, they may be found up to heights of 0.5 m, amongst algae, lichens and mosses on tree trunks, especially when atmospheric humidity is high. Rare in Britain, having been recorded only from wooded areas in Worcestershire, Herefordshire and Shropshire, all within approximately 10 miles of Bewdley in the Wyre Forest. They appear to feed on soft dead vegetable matter.

The biology of the British caddis flies is reviewed by Hickin (1967) and a key to adults of the British species is given by Macan (1973). An RES Handbook to adult caddis is available (Barnard & Ross, 2012). Two AIDGAP guides have been published: to caddis larvae (Wallace, 2006) and to adult caddis (Barnard & Ross, 2008).

Phylum MOLLUSCA

Class Gastropoda

The gastropods have traditionally been divided into four groups, with two of these represented in British terrestrial habitats: Pulmonata and Prosobranchia. Pulmonata have lungs and are adapted for a terrestrial life, whereas most prosobranch species are gilled and more suited for an aquatic existence. Not surprisingly, of the 115 terrestrial gastropod species encountered in Britain only 2 are prosobranchs, and these can be distinguished from the pulmonate snails by their having a horny 'lid' – the operculum – which is used to seal off the shell aperture when the animal retreats. All of the remaining species, both slugs and snails, are pulmonates. The snails are instantly recognisable from other groups of animals because of their shells, and slugs can be distinguished by their tentacles. The distinction between slugs and snails is less clear-cut. Some 'snails' have very small shells, whereas one family of 'slugs' – the carnivorous slugs (family Testacellidae) – has a rudimentary shell.

Two AIDGAP keys are available: to land snails (Cameron & Riley, 2008) and to slugs (Rowson *et al.*, 2014).

References

Note. SBF refers to the *Synopses of the British Fauna* series published by Field Studies Council on behalf of the Linnean Society of London. RES refers to the *Handbooks for the Identification of British Insects* series published by Field Studies Council on behalf of the Royal Entomological Society. Volumes in both series may be obtained from Field Studies Council.

AGUILAR, J ., DOMMANGET, J.-L., and PRÉCHAC. (1986) *A field guide to the Dragonflies of Britain, Europe and North Africa.* Collins.

ARCHER, M.E. (2014) *The vespoid wasps.* RES Vol.6, part 6.

ARTHUR, D.R. (1963) *British Ticks.* Butterworths.

BALL, I.R. and REYNOLDSON, T.B. (1981) *British Planarians.* SBF **19**.

BALL, S. and MORRIS, R. (2013) *Britain's hoverflies: an introduction to the hoverflies of Britain.* Wildguides, Princeton University Press.

BARBER, A.D. (2008): *Key to the identification of British centipedes.* AIDGAP, Field Studies Council.

BARBER, A.D. (2009): *Centipedes.* SBF **58**.

BARNARD, P.C. (2011) *The Royal Entomological Society Book of British Insects.* Wiley.

BARNARD, P.C. and ROSS, E. (2008) *Guide to the adult caddisflies or sedge flies (Trichoptera)* AIDGAP, Field Studies Council.

BARNARD, P.C. and ROSS, E. (2012) *The adult Trichoptera (caddisflies) of Britain and Ireland.* RES Vol. 1, part 17.

BEBBINGTON, J. & LEWINGTON, R. (1998) *Guide to the butterflies of Britain.* OP48, Field Studies Council.

BEE, L. & LEWINGTON, R. (2002) *Guide to house and garden spiders.* OP69, Field Studies Council.

BETTS, C., LAFFOLLEY, D. D'A. & CRIBB, P.W. (1986) *The Hymenopterist's Handbook* (2nd ed). Amateur Entomologists Society.

BLACKMAN, R.L. (2010) *Aphids - Aphidinae (Macrosiphini)* RES Vol. 2, Part 7.

BLOWER, J.G. (1985) *Millipedes.* SBF **35**.

BRINDLE, A. (1977) British earwigs. *Entomologist's Gazette* **28**.

BRISTOWE, W.S. (1958) *The world of spiders.* New Naturalist series. Collins.

BROOKS, S. & ASKEW, R. (1999) *Guide to dragonflies and damselflies of Britain.* OP53, Field Studies Council.

BROWN, V.K. (1983) *Grasshoppers.* Cambridge University Press.

BROWN, P., ROY, H.E., COMONT, R., POLAND, R. & SHIELDS, C. (2012) *Guide to the ladybird larvae of the British Isles.* OP152, Field Studies Council.

BUGLIFE, O'TOOLE, C. & SHIELDS, C. (2007) *Bees of Britain.* OP119, Field Studies Council.

CAMERON, R.A.D. and RILEY, G. (2008) *Land snails in the British Isles* (2nd ed.) AIDGAP, Field Studies Council.

CHAM, S. (2012) *Field guide to the larvae and exuviae of British Dragonflies (Anisoptera) and Damselflies (Zygoptera)* British Dragonfly Society.

CHANDLER, P. (2010) *A Dipterists' Handbook.* Amateur Entomologists' Society.

CLAY, T. (1969) A key to the genera of Menoponidae (Amblycera: Mallophaga: Insecta) *Bulletin of the British Museum (Natural History) (Ent.)* **24**: 1-26.

CLAY, T. (1970) The Amblycera (Phthiraptera: Insecta) *Bulletin of the British Museum (Natural History) (Ent.)* **25**: 75-98.

CHINERY, M. (2012) *Insects of Britain and Western Europe.* A&C Black.

CLOUDSLEY-THOMPSON, J.L. and SANKEY, J. (1961) *Land Invertebrates.* Methuen.

COLYER, C.N. and HAMMOND, C.O. (1968) *Flies of the British Isles* (2nd ed.) Wayside and Woodland Series. Frederick Warne.

COOTER, J. and BARCLAY, M.V.L. (2006) *A Coleopterist's Handbook* (4th Ed.) Amateur Entomologists' Society.

CORBET, P.S., LONGFIELD, C. and MOORE, N.W. (1960) *Dragonflies*. New Naturalist Series. Collins.

CROWSON, R.A. (1981) *The Biology of the Coleoptera*. Academic Press.

DALLIMORE, T. and SHAW, P. (2013) *Illustrated key to the families of British Springtails (Collembola)* AIDGAP, Field Studies Council.

DELANEY, M.J. (1954) *Thysanura and Diplura*. Handbooks for the Identification of British Insects. Vol. 1, Part 2. Royal Entomological Society.

DUFF, A.G. (2012) *Beetles of Britain and Ireland. Vol. 1: Sphaeriusidae to Silphidae*. A.G. Duff Publishing.

EASON, E.H. (1964) *Centipedes of the British Isles*. Frederick Warne.

EDWARDS, C.A. (1959) A revision of the British Symphyla. *Proceedings of the Zoological Society of London*, **132**: 403-439.

EDWARDS, C.A. and LOFTY, J.R. (1972) *The biology of earthworms* (2nd ed.) Chapman & Hall.

EDWARDS, M. & JENNER, M. (2009) *Field guide to the bumblebees of Great Britain and Ireland*. Ocelli.

ELLIOT, J.M. and HUMPESCH, U.H. (1983) *A key to the adults of the British Ephemeroptera*. Scientific Publication **47**, Freshwater Biological Association.

ELLIOT, J.M. and MANN, K.H. (1979) *A key to the British freshwater leeches*. Scientific Publication **40**, Freshwater Biological Association.

EVANS, G.O., SHEALS, J.G. and MACFARLANE, D. (1961) *The terrestrial Acari of the British Isles. An introduction to their morphology, biology and classification. Vol. 1. Introduction and biology.* British Museum (Natural History)

EVANS, M. and EDMONSON, R. (2005) *A photographic guide to the shieldbugs and squashbugs of the British Isles* (2nd ed) Wild Guide UK.

FERRIS, G.F. (1961) *The sucking lice*. Pacific Coast Entomological Society.

FORD, E.B. (1957) *Butterflies* (3rd ed.) New Naturalist Series **1**. Collins.

FOSTER, G.N. and FRIDAY, L.E. (2011) *Key to adults of the water beetles of Britain and Ireland (Part 1)* RES Vol. 4, part 5.

FOSTER, G.N., BILTON, D.T. and FRIDAY, L.E. (2011) *Key to adults of the water beetles of Britain and Ireland (Part 2)* RES Vol. 4, part 5b.

GIBBONS, B. (1986) *Dragonflies and Damselflies of Britain and Northern Europe*. Hamlyn.

GIBSON, R. (1994) *British Nemerteans* (2nd ed.) SBF **24**.

GILBERT, F.S. (1986) *Hoverflies*. Naturalists' Handbooks, Cambridge University Press.

GISIN, H. (1960) *Collembolenfaunas Europas*. Museum d'Histoire Naturelle, Geneva (German text)

GOODEY, T. (1963) *Soil and Freshwater Nematodes*. 2nd ed. (revised by J. B. Goodey) Methuen.

GREGORY, S. (2009) *Woodlice and Waterlice (Isopoda: Oniscidea & Asellota) in Britain and Ireland*. Biological Records Centre / Field Studies Council.

GURNEY, R. (1931) *British Freshwater Copepods*. Vols I, II and III. Ray Society.

HAMMOND, C. O. (1985) *The Dragonflies of the British Isles* (2nd ed.) Harley Books.

HARDE, K.W. and HAMMOND, P.W. (1984) *A Field Guide in Colour to Beetles*. Octopus Books.

HARDING, J.P. and SMITH, W.A. (1960) *A key to the British Freshwater Cyclopoid and Calanoid Copepods*. Scientific Publication **18**, Freshwater Biological Association.

HEATH, J. and EMMET, A.M. (eds) (1976) *The moths and butterflies of Great Britain and Ireland*. 11 volumes, 4 completed. Harley Books.

HICKIN, N.E. (1967) *Caddis larvae*. Hutchinson.

HILLYARD, P.D. (1996): *Ticks of North-West Europe*. SBF **52**.

HILLYARD, P.D. (2005): *Harvestmen* (3rd ed.) SBF **4**.

HINCKS, W.D. (1956) *Dermaptera and Orthoptera*. RES, Vol. 1, Part 5.

HOPKIN, S.P. (1991) *A key to the woodlice of Britain and Ireland*. AIDGAP, Field Studies Council.

HOPKIN, S.P. (2003) *The woodlouse name trail*. OP75, Field Studies Council.

HOPKIN, S.P. (2007) *A key to the Collembola (Springtails) of Britain and Ireland*. AIDGAP, Field Studies Council.

HOPKIN, S.P. and READ, H.J. (1992) *The biology of millipedes.* Oxford University Press.
HOPKIN, S.P. and ROBERTS, A.W. (1988) Symphyla – the least studied of the most interesting soil animals. *Bulletin of the British Myriapod Group* **5**: 28-34.
HUBBLE, D. (2012) *Keys to the adults of seed and leaf beetles.* AIDGAP, Field Studies Council.
HYNES, H.B.N. (1977) *A key to the adults and nymphs of the British stoneflies.* Scientific Publication **17** (3rd ed.) Freshwater Biological Association.
JACKSON, R.N. and RAW, F. (1966) *Life in the Soil.* Institute of Biology Studies in Biology **2**. Arnold.
JONES-WALTERS (1989) *Keys to families of British spiders.* AIDGAP, Field Studies Council.
JOY, N.H. (1932) *A Practical Handbook of British Beetles* (2 vols) Reprinted in 1976 by E.W. Classey.
KEEN, D. (1977) *Collecting and studying Dragonflies.* Amateur Entomologist's Society **12**.
KEVAN, D.K. McE. (1962) *Soil Animals.* H. F. & G. Witherby.
KIRK, W.D.J. (1996) Thrips. Naturalists' Handbook 25. Richmond Publishing Company.
LEE, P. (2006) Atlas of the Millipedes (Diplopoda) of Britain and Ireland. Biological Records Centre / Pensoft.
LEGG, G. and JONES, P.E. (1988) Pseudoscorpions. SBF **40**.
LEVEY, B. (2009) *British Scraptiidae.* RES Vol. 5, part 18.
LEWINGTON, R. (2003) *Pocket guide to the butterflies of Great Britain and Ireland.* British Wildlife Publishing.
LEWIS, J.G.E. (2007) *The biology of centipedes* (New ed.) Cambridge University Press.
LEWIS, T. (1973) *Thrips.* Academic Press.
LINCOLN, R.J. (1979) *British Marine Amphipoda: Gammaridea.* British Museum (Natural History)
LINSSEN, R.F. (1959) *Beetles of the British Isles* (2 volumes) Frederick Warne.
LOCKET, G.H. and MILLEDGE, A.F. (1951-53) *British Spiders*, Vols 1 & 2. Ray Society.
LOCKET, G.H., MILLEDGE, A.F. and MERRETT, P. (1974) *British Spiders*, Vol. 3. Ray Society.
LOTT, D.A. (2009) The Staphylinidae (rove beetles) of Britain and Ireland (Part 5). RES. Vol. 12, part 5.
LOTT, D.A. & ANDERSON, R. (2011) The Staphylinidae (rove beetles) of Britain and Ireland (Parts 7 & 8). RES. Vol. 12, parts 7 & 8.
LUFF, M.L. (2007) *The Carabidae (ground beetles) of Britain and Ireland* (2nd ed) RES Vol. 4, Part 2.
MACADAM, C. & BENNETT, C. (2010) *A Pictorial Guide to British Ephemeroptera.* AIDGAP, Field Studies Council.
MACAN, T.T. (1969) *The study of mayflies (Ephemeroptera)* Amateur Entomologist's Society **31**.
MACAN, T.T. (1973) *A key to the adults of the British Trichoptera.* Scientific Publication **28**, Freshwater Biological Association.
MACAN, T.T. (1982) *The study of stoneflies, mayflies and caddis flies.* The Amateur Entomologist **17**.
MAJERUS, M. (2002) Moths. New Naturalist Series **90**. Collins.
MAJERUS, M., ROY, H.E., BROWN, P., POLAND, R. & SHIELDS, C. (2006) *Guide to the ladybirds of the British Isles.* OP102, Field Studies Council.
MANN, K.H. (1962) *Leeches. Their structure, physiology, ecology and embryology.* Pergamon.
MANN, K.H. (1964) *A key to the British freshwater leeches with notes on their ecology.* Scientific Publication **28**, Freshwater Biological Association.
MARSHALL, J. and HAES, C. (1990) *Grasshoppers and allied insects of Great Britain and Ireland.* Harley Books.
MARSHALL, J. & OVENDEN D. (1999) *Guide to British grasshoppers and allied insects.* OP54, Field Studies Council.
McGEERY, A. (1986) *A complete guide to British Dragonflies.* Jonathan Cape.
MORRIS, M.G. (1997) *Broad-nosed weevils.* RES. Vol. 5, part 17a.
MORRIS, M.G. (2002) *True weevils (part 1)* RES. Vol. 5, part 17b.
MORRIS, M.G. (2008) *True Weevils (part 2)* RES. Vol. 5, part 17c.
MORRIS, M.G. (2012) *True Weevils (part 3)* RES. Vol. 5, part 17d.

MOUND, L.A., MORISON, G.D., PITKIN, B.R. and PALMER, J.M. (1976) *Thysanoptera*. RES. Vol. 1, part 11.

NAU, B. (2004) *Guide to the shieldbugs of the British Isles*. OP85, Field Studies Council.

NEW, T.R. (2006) *Pscoids Psocoptera (Booklice and barklice)* RES. Vol. 1, part 7.

NEWLAND, D.E., STILL, R. and TOMLINSON, D. (2010) *Britain's butterflies: a field guide to the butterflies of Britain and Ireland*. Wildguides, Princeton University Press.

NOSEK, J. (1973) *The European Protura, their taxonomy, ecology and distribution with keys for determination*. Museum d'Histoire Naturelle, Geneva (English text)

O'CONNOR, F.B. (1967) The Enchytraeidae. In *Soil Biology* (A. Burges & F. Raw, eds), pp. 212-257. Academic Press.

OLIVER, P.G. and MEECHAN, C.J. (1993): *Woodlice*. SBF **45**. Linnean Society.

PANTIN, C.F.A. (1969) *The genus* Geonemertes. Bulletin of the British Museum (Natural History) (Zoology) **18**: 263-310.

PLANT, C.W. (1997) A key to the adults of British lacewings and their allies (Neuroptera, Megaloptera, Raphidiptera and Mecoptera) AIDGAP, Field Studies Council.

PRYCE, D., MACADAM, C. and BROOKS, S. (2007) *Guide to the British Stonefly (Plecoptera) families: adults and larvae*. AIDGAP, Field Studies Council.

PRYS-JONES, O.E. and CORBET, S.A. (2011) *Bumblebees* (3rd ed.). Naturalists' Handbooks, Pelagic Publishing.

RAGGE, D.R. (1965) *Grasshoppers, Crickets and Cockroaches of the British Isles* Wayside and Woodland Series. Frederick Warne.

RICHARDS, O.W. (1977) *Hymenoptera: Introduction and key to the families*. RES. Vol. 6, part 1 (2nd ed.)

RICHARDS, P. (2010) *Guide to harvestmen of the British Isles*. OP140, Field Studies Council.

ROBERTS, M.J. (1995) *Spiders of Britain and Northern Europe*. Collins.

ROWSON, B., TURNER, J., ANDERSON R. and SYMONDSON, B. (2014) *Slugs of Britain and Ireland*. AIDGAP, Field Studies Council.

SHERLOCK, E. (2012) *Key to the earthworms of the UK and Ireland*. AIDGAP, Field Studies Council

SIMS, R.W. and GERARD, B.M. (1999) *Earthworms* (revised) SBF **31**. Linnean Society.

SKIDMORE, P. (1989) *Insects of the cow dung community*. AIDGAP, Field Studies Council.

SKINNER, B. (1984) *Moths of the British Isles*. Viking Books.

SKINNER, G.J. & ALLEN, G.W. (2013) *Ants* Naturalists' Handbook. Pelagic Publishing.

SMALLSHIRE, D. and SWASH, A. (2014) *Britain's Dragonflies: A field guide to the damselflies and dragonflies of Britain and Ireland* (2nd ed) Wildguides, Princeton University Press.

STERLING, P., PARSONS, M. and LEWINGTON, R. (2012) *Field guide to the micro-moths of Great Britain and Ireland*. British Wildlife Publishing.

STUBBS, A.E. and DRAKE, M. (2014) *British hoverflies – an illustrated identification guide* (2nd ed.). British Entomological and Natural History Society.

STUBBS, A.E. and FALK, S.J. (2002) *British Soldierflies and Their Allies: A Field Guide to the Larger British Brachycera* (2nd ed.) British Entomological and Natural History Society.

SOUTHWOOD, T.R.E. and LESTON, D. (1959) *Land and water bugs of the British Isles*. Wayside and Woodland Series. Frederick Warne.

UNWIN, D. M. (1981) A key to the families of British Diptera. *Field Studies*, **5**(3): 513-544. AIDGAP, Field Studies Council.

UNWIN, D.M. (1984) *A key to the families of British Coleoptera (beetles) and Strepsiptera*. AIDGAP, Field Studies Council.

UNWIN, D.M. (2001) *A key to families of British bugs (Insecta, Hemiptera)*. AIDGAP, Field Studies Council.

WALSH, G.B. and DIBB, J.R. (1953: 1975) *A Coleopterist's Handbook*. First printed 1953, revised by Cooter, J. and Cribb, P. W. (1975) Amateur Entomologist's Society.

WANLESS, F.R. (1977) On the occurrence of the scorpion *Euscorpius flavicaudis* (DeGeer) at Sheerness Port, Isle of Sheppey, Kent. *Bulletin of the British Arachnological Society* **4**: 74-76.

WALLACE, I. (2006) *Simple key to caddis larvae.* AIDGAP, Field Studies Council.

WARING, P., TOWNSEND, M. and LEWINGTON, R. (2009) *Field guide to the moths of Great Britain and Ireland* (2nd ed.) British Wildlife Publishing.

WHEATER, C.P. and READ, H.J. (1996) *Animals under logs and stones.* Naturalists' Handbook 22. Richmond Publishing Company.

WHEATER, C.P. and COOK, P.A. (2003) *Studying invertebrates.* Naturalists' Handbook 28. Richmond Publishing Company.

WHITAKER, A.P. (2007) *Fleas (Siphonaptera)* RES. Vol. 1, part 16. Royal Entomological Society.

WILLMER, P. (1985) *Bees, ants and wasps. A key to the genera of the British Aculeates.* AIDGAP, Field Studies Council.

WRIGHT, A. (1990) *British sawflies.* AIDGAP, Field Studies Council.

YEO, P.F. and CORBET, S.A. (1995). *Solitary Wasps* (2nd ed.) Naturalists' Handbook 3. Richmond Publishing Company.

Index

The index shows where groups of animals key out followed by the page number where the morphological and ecological notes can be found.

Scorpiones C17: 55
Scorpions C17: 55
Scutigeromorpha 72
Shieldbugs 67
Silverfish 63
Siphonaptera B13, D13, D44: 74
Slugs B4: 76
Snakeflies D45, F23: 74
Snails B2: 75
Snow fleas D36: 72
Spiders C18: 56
Springtails D5; D27, D43: 62
Squashbugs 68
Sternorrhyncha 68
Stick insects D35: 67
Stoneflies F18, F26: 67
Strepsiptera E4: 75
Stylops 75
Sucking lice D47: 68
Symphyla C7: 61
Symphyta D7, D9, F26: 71

Talitridae 58
Talitroides (= *Arcitalitrus*) 58
Termites 65
Tettigonioidea 66
Tetrigoidea 66
Three-pronged bristletails D23: 63
Thrips D50, F8: 69
Thunderflies 70
Thysanoptera D50, F8: 69
Thysanura D23: 63
Ticks C19: 57
Treehoppers 67
Trichoptera D3, D38: F20: 75
Trocheta subviridis 54
True flies B11, B12, B13, B14, B16, D52, E3,
    E4: 70
True lice 68
Turbellaria B6: 53
Two-pronged bristletails D28: 62

Wasps B14, D32, F17: 71
Water bugs 67
Weevils B11: 69
Whiteflies F2: 67
Whiteworms B16: 54
Wingless adult beetles D7, D19, D40: 69
Wingless female caddis flies D38: 75
Wingless female moths D34: 72
Wingless flies D52: 70

Woodlice C5: 58
Wood-boring beetles B9: 69

Zygentoma 63
Zygoptera 64